Nicky Hooks and Sharon Burnett (who, although not quite a Gestalt entity, are in fact joined at the hip) met in 1983, when Sharon moved from Dagenham to Braintree in Essex and started work at the same branch of a certain supermarket. In 1991 Nicky finally succumbed to Sharon's constant nagging, and, thinking 'Anything for a quiet life,' she decided to watch Series IV of *Red Dwarf*. Needless to say, she soon became hooked. After watching two episodes of Series VI being recorded, Nicky decided the time had come to quiz Sharon on her extensive knowledge of Rimmer, Lister and Co., and so *The Red Dwarf Quiz Book* was born. Over the six months it took to compile *A Question of Smeg* they survived on a staple diet of tuna-fish sandwiches and Twiglets.

The Red Dwarf Quiz Book is also published by Penguin.

A QUESTION OF SMEG

THE 2ND RED DWARF™ QUIZ BOOK

SHARON BURNETT AND NICKY HOOKS

PENGUIN BOOKS

PENGUIN BOOKS

Published by the Penguin Group
Penguin Books Ltd, 27 Wrights Lane, London W8 5TZ, England
Penguin Books USA Inc., 375 Hudson Street, New York, New York 10014, USA
Penguin Books Australia Ltd, Ringwood, Victoria, Australia
Penguin Books Canada Ltd, 10 Alcorn Avenue, Toronto, Ontario, Canada M4V 3B2
Penguin Books (NZ) Ltd, 182–190 Wairau Road, Auckland 10, New Zealand

Penguin Books Ltd, Registered Offices: Harmondsworth, Middlesex, England

First published 1997
1 3 5 7 9 10 8 6 4 2

Set in 11/14 pt Monotype Bembo
Typeset by Rowland Phototypesetting Limited, Bury St Edmunds, Suffolk
Printed in England by Clays Ltd, St Ives plc

To Mark and Andy – again

Inventory

Inventory

Acknowledgements

Our many thanks to everyone at Grant Naylor Productions. Special thanks to Ray Lavidge for his invaluable help with the puzzles (love that disk!). Also, we would like to thank our husbands, Andy Burnett and Mark Hooks, for their infinite patience.

THE QUESTIONS

Staircase 1

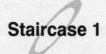

When the words listed below are placed horizontally and in the correct order within the grid, they will spell out diagonally (in the boxes marked in bold) another word from *Red Dwarf*.

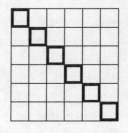

QUASAR
STOCKY
MELLIE
PLANET
XPRESS
SATURN

3

'Glory or insanity awaits!'
Rimmer, 'Holoship'

1 What happens to Kryten when Rimmer goes into 'official mode'?
2 Who was thrown into a cell with Lister and the Cat?
3 Who throws like a 'geek'?
4 According to Rimmer, who had brains of diarrhoea and the breeding of a maggot?
5 Which switch dismantles a bazookoid?
6 According to Lister, what do you call Rimmer when you want to be mega-polite?
7 What did 'Cheat 1' do?
8 What colour is the two-pound ribbed knobbler?
9 Who was the fourth Marx Brother?
10 Who told Lister that Rimmer had failed his engineering exam by writing 'I am a fish' four hundred times?
11 Where did Rimmer exit 'quicker than a whippet with a bum full of dynamite'?
12 According to Confidence, where was Paranoia?
13 What does 'otrozone' do?
14 What did Lister call his English mansion?
15 How wide was the 'giant pizza'?
16 What time was it when the skutters were painting the ship Military Grey?
17 What supplies did Kryten suggest they take into the service ducts?
18 Which song did Lister play 'for the road'?

19 When were the 'Equal Rights for Men' marches?

20 What extra items are turning up in the dirty laundry basket?

21 What had happened to Lister's photos of his eighteenth birthday?

22 What did a 'white card' mean?

23 When did Kryten think the crossbow might come in handy?

24 What footwear did Rimmer suggest Lister should wear to meet the girls aboard the *Nova 5*?

25 What was the 'painting' of Lister's that Rimmer thought was rubbish?

26 How long did Lister intend to be away before he and Rimmer were marooned?

27 What did Able use to engulf the *Centauri*?

28 How many floors is it from the cargo decks to the science room?

29 Who was the father of the Cat People?

30 Where had the archaeologists discovered an alleged missing page from the Bible?

31 Who originally had the confidence and paranoia theory?

32 What had Kryten excluded from the shut-down override aboard *Starbug*?

33 Who had launched himself from his own clay pigeon machine?

34 What was wrong with Rimmer's discourse on 'porous circuits'?

35 How much had the armed raider forced the bank staff to place in the vault?

36 What was Kryten's code name during the wax war?

37 What did Kryten use to kill the thing that was skuttling around the cargo deck?

38 According to Rimmer, why had Lister wanted to go on to the officers' deck?

39 How did Lister, Cat and Kryten escape from the quarantine suite?

40 Where was the Bible's missing page being carbon-dated?

41 From which book warehouse did Lee Harvey Oswald plan to shoot President Kennedy?

42 What sets off the *Red Dwarf*'s sprinkler system?

43 According to Rimmer, who sounded like 'Paul Robeson on dope'?

44 What mark did 'Cloister' give the Cat Priest?

45 Which member of the crew has to justify himself first?

46 According to the log, how many vomit bags were the crew down to?

47 How did Rimmer penalize Lister for saying 'check' in a variety of silly voices while doing the homogenized puddings?

48 How much had been forced into Kryten's wallet at knifepoint?

49 Which rock band did Lister have a T-shirt advertising?

50 Who put the bomb in Adolf Hitler's briefcase?

51 How long did Kryten think it would take him to come up with the outline of a winning case for Rimmer?

52 When Lister 'borrowed' Rimmer's shirt, what did he spill down it?

53 What did the note inside locker 58 read?

54 Who was Section Chief of CGI?

55 How did the Rimmers think the 'No Smoking' signs looked?

56 What did Lister need to gargle with after being kissed by Caroline Carmen?

57 What was the first book that Lister burnt?

58 Why was Fiji three feet below sea level?

59 Who had hex vision other than Rimmer and Dr Lanstrom?

60 What is the symbol for infinity?

61 According to Rimmer, what does his 'H' stand for?

62 What was the 'enemy of democracy' stealing?

63 How long did the engineering exam last?

64 What duties did Lister threaten to give Rimmer when he became an officer?

65 Who can't stand front-seat drivers?

66 Who went missing from Miss Bennett's party?

67 When Rimmer had been with the Jupiter Mining Corporation for fifteen years, how long had Lister served?

68 Who taught foundation courses in Advanced Rebellion?

69 At what age did Rimmer leave home?

70 Who had made Rimmer's Armées du Nord?

71 Who did Rimmer refer to as 'el dirtball'?

72 What was J.F.K. Airport originally called?

73 According to Lister, how did the Egyptians move such massive pieces of stone without the aid of modern technology?

74 What was the only way that Rimmer could join the crew of the *Enlightenment*?

75 Why did Lister want to become a chef?

76 How many years' statutory penalty does the count of murder carry?

77 Where did the time drive take the crew instead of the Taj Mahal Tandoori?

78 For how many counts had Rimmer reported Lister for 'insulting a superior technician'?

79 According to Rimmer, where was Kennedy's Achilles' heel?

80 What did Rimmer think Kryten and Lister might do for an encore?

81 Which of Rimmer's possessions had Lister used as an ashtray?

82 Why did Lister award 'Rimmer' his First Officer decoration?

83 When was Rimmer totally naked except for a pair of mock leather driving gloves and a pair of blue swimming goggles?

84 Who did the Cat describe as 'the human equivalent of a visible panty line'?

85 Why don't the 'high' crew need weapons?

86 According to Rimmer, how many times had Lister committed 'dereliction of duty'?

87 Who looks worse than the Grim Reaper's passport photo?

88 According to Lister, where would any self-respecting bachelor keep his socks?

89 Who did the pavement artist sell Lister's 'Jackson Pollock' to?

90 Who's got orange feet?

91 What was the 'decative'?

92 When did Rimmer laugh so hard he nearly puked?

93 How many Greek soldiers were inside the Trojan Horse?

94 What are the odds of dealing four aces in a row?

95 How long did the crew have to find the second triplicator?

96 Who had personal habits that would make a monkey blush?

97 How many years' imprisonment was President Kennedy sentenced to?

98 According to Rimmer, what's the thing you have to remember about Captain Oates?

99 What did Lister of Smeg claim as his prize for beating the Good Knight?

100 How many people had Rimmer spoken to while he was in the Samaritans?

101 What is the average rainfall in the oil-rich coastal lowlands of Venezuela?

102 Where was Rimmer when he decided that he wanted to be left on while Lister was in stasis?

103 Who put baby Lister in a box under the grav-pool table?

104 What was Space Corps Directive 39436175880932/C?

Crossword 1
'Backwards'

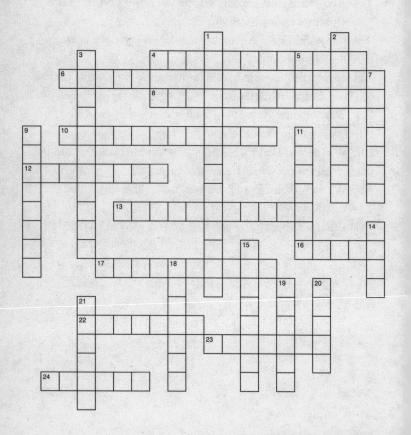

The Questions

Across

4 Billy-Joe's call-sign (6,6)
6 Tranter's valet (5)
8 Virus antidote (4,9)
10 Crew's meeting-place (7,5)
12 Hillbilly's cousin (5,3)
13 Ace's goal (4,7)
16 — Pherson (5)
17 Agonoid (5,5)
22 Mechanical warrior (7)
23 Ace's smoke (7)
24 Tranter's nickname (3,3)

Down

1 Tranter's nickname (7,7)
2 Ace's rank (9)
3 Lister reversed (6,5)
5 Apocalypse horseman (3)
7 Bungo's secretary (7)
9 Project — (8)
11 Tranter's tipple (4,3)
14 Zack's brother (4)
15 Skipper (8)
18 Tranter's rank (7)
19 Test base (6)
20 Famine's brother (5)
21 Apocalypse boy (6)

'I've forgotten what I was going to say!'
Holly, 'Queeg'

State the characters in *Red Dwarf* who said the following, and in which episode.

1 'I think there's something wrong with the gearbox.'
2 'Is it a sort of Cat being smacked on the head by a smegged-off Lister's fist kind of noise?'
3 'If you've got a complaint just come straight out with it, don't hide behind innuendo and hyperbole.'
4 'Kryten, can this story maybe wait, ideally until after I'm dead?'
5 'Why would a haddock kill itself? Why am I even asking that question?'
6 'You should write a letter to *Playboy*, bud. I bet you anything it would get printed.'
7 'If I knew this was gonna happen I would have had an egg sarnie and finished the Cinzano.'
8 'Morning, Lister. How's life in hippy heaven, you pregnant, baboon-bellied space beatnik?'
9 'Just had to say one last goodbye.'
10 'No more troughing.'
11 'Yeah, look on the bright side, at least now I'm only half-crap.'
12 'Er, Lister, "okay" is never a threat, no matter how many A's you put on the end.'
13 'I've seen her naked!'

14 'Well, thankfully Holly's unaffected.'

15 'Somebody please, get me a tailor!'

16 'You're a total dinglebat, aren't you?'

17 'I was lying. It's only a thousand fathoms.'

18 'Save us, somebody save us before I wet me keks!'

19 'SEX, I really want it! SEX, I want to get it! SEX, I think I've found it!'

20 'I don't believe you would ever say anything that I would consider jerky.'

21 'I'm not a cartoonivor.'

22 'Ecstasy! We're talking mega ecstasy bliss!'

23 'What's gotten into you guys? This is like Saturday night at the Wailing Wall.'

24 'Abandon shop. This is not a daffodil. Repeat, this is not a daffodil.'

25 'Holly, wipe the rabid foam from your chin and start again.'

26 'How am I supposed to concentrate on a phasing comet when as soon as my back is turned the salad cream gets warm?'

27 'Let the orgy commence.'

28 'Got to admit, bud, got a handle on you there.'

29 'What do you say, motherboarder?'

30 'Please, Ace, don't go. I love you.'

31 'Give that man an eyebrow. Hey, I'm feeling generous, give him two.'

32 'Shut your stupid, flat head.'

33 'Fearsome! I was fearsome!'

34 'Welcome to the Starlight Ballroom. Hey, fly me to the moon and let me . . .'

35 'Rimmer, have sex with someone, and that's an order.'

36 'We may as well have been playing tennis.'
37 'Just cross-filing that story under B for blackmail and A for anecdote, sub-category S for so funny you'll laugh till you're sick.'
38 'If you weren't my friend I'd steal your shoes.'
39 'Has anybody got any whipped cream?'
40 'One minute you're down, the next you're right back up again.'
41 'I, the smeg, am Lister.'
42 'Charge, my hordes of darkness. Bring me the head of the despicable one.'
43 'Oh, well done, bud. Now we'll have to do the washing-up.'
44 'You scoundrels! Return my bike immediately.'
45 'We'd better be going. The moons will be setting in a bit.'
46 'Miss Kochanski, who d'you think, Madame Curie?'
47 'Now that's the kind of cash that opens anybody's legs.'
48 'Good evening, you stupid, stinking, festering gimboid of a cat.'
49 'First moon we come to, let's dump her.'
50 'Hi, killer.'
51 'I would like to purchase that orange inflatable beach ball and that small bucket and spade.'
52 'It leaves us galloping up diarrhoea drive without a saddle.'
53 'Florence Nightingdroid, could I have a word?'
54 'Hey, you're a work of art, baby!'
55 'What's he going to do, drop his trousers?'
56 'You come anywhere near me, buddy, and you'll be wearing them bowels as a bobble hat.'

57 'When it really comes down to it, you're one heck of a regular guy.'

58 'Hey, I'm looking so good today. If I looked any better I'd be illegal.'

59 'We've been copied more times than that poster of the tennis girl scratching her butt.'

60 'Well, of course you do have a small physical presence.'

61 'Let's talk about this, shall we? Over a pot of tea and some toasted muffins.'

62 'There's no point in running, Lister. It's mine. I found it. I've got bagsies.'

63 'What have I got to lose, me jar?'

64 'Never mind the stabilizers, where's the hair mousse?'

65 'Well, this is a turn-up, innit? You'd better boogie on over and we can sort it out.'

66 'Last one alive's a wet ponce.'

67 'Hello, wall. What do you think?'

68 'You've squeezed all the ketchup out of my burger.'

69 'Tell me again, how do you hang ten?'

70 'It's got a brilliant ending. I could hardly believe my nose.'

71 'Is that female as in soft and squidgy?'

72 'If he tells me to take it easy one more time, I swear I'm gonna turn his ears into a pair of maracas and tap dance a fandango on his throat.'

73 'Now, I've packed all your heads. They're in the bag.'

74 'I am on the case, I'm sharp, I'm kicking bottom.'

75 'Actually, Flash, that might be a bit of a problem.'

76 'So she's not as attractive as me, then?'

77 'For crying out loud, Rimmer!'

78 'Going down.'

79 'We're grooving tonight. Ahead, groove factor five.'

80 'Perhaps I didn't make myself clear. I said supper is ready.'

81 'Keep writing those hits, kid.'

82 'I am your God.'

83 'I'll make a note, ma'am. *Now Voyager* worth keeping on stand-by.'

84 'Kryten, isn't it round about this time of year your head goes back to the lab for re-tuning?'

85 'Hey, old Five Fingers has checked out.'

86 'Aye, sling your bloody hook. Clear off!'

87 'Oh, Rimmer, you *are* a smeghead.'

88 'The only thing I've ever seen pick up slower is Rimmer in a disco.'

89 'Who'd steal a gigantic red trash can with no brakes and three million years on the clock?'

90 'Shakespeare? Who's Shakespeare?'

91 'Goodbye, Ace Rimmer. You were a most worthy adversary.'

92 'Two and one half badgers please. No, I'll eat them here.'

93 'Human, lovely with a bit of mint sauce.'

'Not all the way through, no, but I can quote some though'
Rimmer, 'Marooned'

State which character said the following, and in which *Red Dwarf* novel.

1 'This bitch is good!'
2 'Aw, hell. I was really looking forward to being dead. I don't deserve any better.'
3 'I'm very proud of you, Son. I'm so proud I'm fit to burst.'
4 'A fine soldier, a good friend – and a hell of a great man.'
5 'Just gloody well giss her gefore they gegin to realize you're not gosher!'
6 'Who the smeg's that? Gurning champion of the century?'
7 'You've been an inspiration to me, sir. Always gave me something to look up to.'
8 'Infinitely more prudent for us to take off in the opposite direction?'
9 'Screw Lister, and quite frankly, Rimmer, screw you.'
10 'Don't be a ponce. Just get the smegging thing back in one piece.'
11 'Mahooooooo!'
12 'Such as, my old sick bucket?'
13 'And that's why you've quit your diet, right?'

14 'Get up, you dozy metal bastard!'

15 'Why on Io would the trigger-happy pork poker bother locking his car up here in this God-forsaken wilderness?'

16 'He won't be dead long.'

17 'The party ain't over till there's only Cinzano left to drink!'

18 'Bugger me, that was noisy.'

19 'Quark dingbat fizzigog Netherlands, Smirk Windo-Kleen double-helix badger.'

20 'Well, old chum-burger, looks like you've got yourself into a bit of a pickle jar and screwed the lid down tight.'

21 'I had me a perfectly good bath straight after Gettysburg.'

22 'Wake up and smell your first early morning dump, Vinegar Drawers!'

23 'Guard it with your life, bud. And I mean your life.'

24 'The only qualification you've got is a certificate entitling you to suck out the nozzles on a chicken soup machine.'

25 'Shut up, you dead git!'

26 'Your call, Ace. I'm just the grease monkey.'

27 'Private bloody party! Our money's as good as anyone's!'

28 'Do I look like a total sex god of the mountains, or what?'

29 'Wow! Does he have balls of steel, or what?'

30 'Who are you calling dead, dog-chew head?'

31 'Pretentious? Watashi?'

32 'Stupid smegging farty stupid shitty shit shit smeg fart poo shit . . .'

33 'I'm a bleeding technishern, don't yew know.'

34 'Buddy, I'm so far ahead of you, you can't see me with
    an atomic-powered telescope.'
35 'Oh shitty death.'
36 'Hey, Frog Prince, I've brought you some breakfast.
    Did you sleep?'
37 'Please, God, someone save me, I don't want to die.'
38 'Check-out time, guys. The A team has arrived.'
39 'He's jealous because you're only fifteen, and you've
    had more sex than him.'
40 'I bet this doesn't work.'
41 'How d'you fight a lamp-post?'
42 'Are you listening to me? I'm not out to lunch, OK?
    None of this is true.'
43 'Nicolette est avec toi.'
44 'Can you give us the votes of the Mercurian jury?'
45 'Penis still isn't big enough.'
46 'No prisoners!'

Word search 1
The *Dwarf*

The words listed opposite are 'hidden' in the grid. They may be found written vertically, horizontally or diagonally, and even backwards.

AUTO DESTRUCT
BLUE MIDGET
CARGO BAY
CINEMA
DIESEL DECKS
DOCKING BAY
DRIVE ROOM
HOLLY
HOLOGRAM SIMULATION
MEDIBAY
NAVICOMP
OBSERVATION DOME
PARROTS BAR
PENTHOUSE
PIPELINE
POST POD
QUARANTINE SUITE
RED DWARF
SCOOP
SKUTTER
STARBUG
STASIS BOOTH
SUPPLIES
VENDING MACHINE
XPRESS LIFT
Z DECK

'Head!'

1 According to Holly, how many words had Lister exchanged with Rimmer before the accident?

2 How many holograms can Holly sustain at one time?

3 What was Holly thinking about when he failed to notice that the crew hadn't returned from the Backwards universe?

4 What did Holly think had happened to Kryten's face?

5 What two new musical notes had Holly invented?

6 What was Holly's fond hope after three million years away from Earth?

7 According to Holly, what is a 'flamingo-up'?

8 Why didn't Holly tell Rimmer the 'alien' pod was a garbage pod?

9 How long was it before Holly noticed that the crew had failed to return from the Backwards universe on schedule?

10 What's the only thing that helps Holly keep his 'slender grip on reality'?

11 Where had Holly lost the polymorph?

12 According to Holly, what's the average time for second class post?

13 What did Holly think the aliens might be able to give Rimmer a hand with?

14 Why couldn't Holly X-ray the cryogenic escape pod to see who was inside?

15 What did Holly think had happened to the black box when he couldn't find it?

16 According to Holly, with compound interest, how much of the world's wealth did Lister possess?

17 What did Rimmer think would run things better on *Red Dwarf* than Holly?

18 What instrument would women have to be banned from playing if Holly's new notes were accepted?

19 What was Holly's remaining run time when she switched herself off?

20 Why did Holly choose *his* face?

Word search 2
'Stoke Me a Clipper'

The words listed opposite are 'hidden' in the grid. They may be found written vertically, horizontally or diagonally, and even backwards.

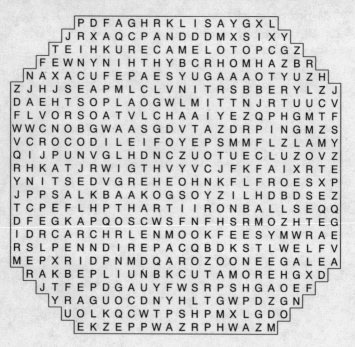

ACE	DISLOCATE
ALLIGATOR	DUNDEE CAKE
ALPHONSE	EUNUCH
ARNIE	GALAHAD
ASTROCUTS	GESTAPO
BACOFOIL	GOALPOST HEAD
BERYL	GOOD KNIGHT
BREAKFAST	HAMSTER
BUTTERFLIES	HERO
CAMELOT	HIGHLIGHTS
CAPTAIN VOORHESE	IRON BALLS
CATERPILLAR	KIPPER
CHASTITY CHEAT	MARIA VON TRAPP
CLIPPER	PRINCESS BONJELLA
CODPIECE	RACHEL
COUGAR	SMOKE
CROCODILE	STOKE
DESTINY	TOASTED MUFFINS
DIMENSION JUMP	WIG

'Ippy dippy, my space shippy . . .'
Lister, 'Me²'

1　How many motor-cyclists escorted Rimmer's limousine?
2　Where had the crew found the time drive?
3　What's *Starbug*'s registration number?
4　How did the crew get from *Red Dwarf* to the *Nova 5*?
5　What was wrong with the old stasis mechanism on *Starbug*?
6　What had the Scouter found in the 'lava' planets' ocean?
7　Why had the *Mayflower* failed to reach the Andromeda Galaxy?
8　How long did Kryten train to pilot *Starbug*?
9　What had the crew discovered just before they lost *Red Dwarf*?
10　How long should it have taken *Red Dwarf* to get back to Earth originally?
11　How long did the prototype craft's black box recording last?
12　How often was there a tour of duty on board the *Mayflower*?
13　What are *Red Dwarf*'s interior doors made of?
14　What was *Starbug*'s viewscreen made of?
15　What is the only way the crew could get to *Starbug*'s back-up generator?
16　How many gear levers does *Blue Midget* have?
17　What had happened to the *Mayflower*?

18 Which ship had a crew of just under two thousand?

19 What did cars in the 23rd century run on?

20 How many deep sleep units were there on board the *Mayflower*?

21 What vehicle did Rimmer first visualize in Better Than Life?

22 Why did Kochanski think that all *Starbug*'s hazard approach lights were flashing?

23 In which vehicle did Kryten learn to drive?

24 How long would it take a duality jump to get the *Nova 5* back to Earth?

25 What was the name of the scout ship the crew had come across frozen into the tundra of an arctic moon?

26 How much had the *Wildfire* test ship cost?

27 Why was *Starbug* withdrawn from service?

28 How long had it taken the crew of the *Nova 5* to find a blue supergiant?

29 How many computer printers are there in *Red Dwarf*'s drive room?

30 What transport did Lister and the Cat steal in the Backwards universe?

31 Where does the hatchway in Lister's shower lead to?

32 According to Rimmer, where do you sit during the crash procedure?

33 What had the nanobots done with *Red Dwarf*?

34 What did the Galactic coordinates mark?

35 What mass did the *Enlightenment* have?

36 How many human crew had there been on board the *Mayflower*?

37 How many spark chambers are there in *Red Dwarf*'s engine?

38 How far in advance had Project Wildfire's test ship returned?

39 How many derelicts were there in the spaceship graveyard?

40 Where does Lister say that the crew keep their secret store of sperm?

41 How many landing jets should *Starbug* have?

42 What type of vehicle did the two Listers steal from the car pound?

43 At what time did *Starbug* have to take off in order to leave the solar system?

44 What had Lister used to unpick the lock of the hillbilly's car?

45 In what type of car did Lister and Rimmer leave Bedford Falls?

46 What was buried deep in the heart of the astral glacier?

47 Where did the second cat ark fly?

48 Where are *Starbug*'s spare fuel tanks?

49 How far had *Starbug* travelled under the lava in four days?

50 What had Lister used to attach the landing jet to *Starbug*?

51 Which book did Lister read while in his hopper waiting for Rimmer?

52 How often do the service ducts on *Starbug* get back-washed?

53 What would you find in hangar 101?

54 What caused the red-hot wound in *Starbug*'s belly?

55 What was *Starbug* designed to do?

56 How long was it before *Starbug* could take off from the Backwards planet for the second time?

57 How long will it take to get *Red Dwarf*'s engines up and running?

58 According to Rimmer, on how many counts would
    Starbug fail the Ministry of Space's minimum safety
    requirements?

59 Where did the crew hide *Starbug* in the Backwards
    universe?

60 What had been the *Mayflower*'s mission?

61 Where did *Wildfire One* land on *Red Dwarf*?

62 Where would Lister abandon his stolen hoppers?

63 How long did it take the shuttle to go from Mimas to
    Red Dwarf?

64 According to Holly, how long would it take *Red Dwarf*
    just to do a fairly sharpish U-turn?

65 What was Project Wildfire?

66 Where had *Red Dwarf*'s black box touched down?

67 Where had Rimmer drunkenly parked his time
    machine?

68 Why wouldn't *Starbug*'s thrusters work?

69 According to the Cat, what can travel at speeds they can
    only dream of?

Crossword 2
'Thanks for the Memory'

Across

2 How many days the crew lost (4)
4 Lister and Cat both acquired one! (7,4)
8 Burial monument (10)
9 How many times Rimmer made love to McGruder (4)
11 Both Lister and Rimmer were in love with her (4,5)
12 Hurts like hell and is below the knee (5)
14 Could this mean 'you'? (6)
15 Rimmer was probably only expecting this (3)

Down

1 Ship's female boxing champion (6,8)
3 Dark carton, perhaps? (5,3)
5 Rimmer is always looking out for them (6)
6 Broken appendage for Cat and Lister (4)
7 Anniversary for Rimmer (8)
10 They're done! (8)
13 — Billy Skank, Lister's favourite music (5)

'Did someone just turn over two pages at once?'
Cat, 'Nanarchy'

This section is based entirely on the *Red Dwarf* novels.

1　Who died at the age of ninety-eight?
2　According to Rimmer, what kind of people live in the most obscure peaks of obscure mountains?
3　What had Rimmer intended to turn Bedford Falls into?
4　Who ran the Undertaker's Parlour in Existence?
5　On Garbage World, what was Lister's sofa made from?
6　How did the Rage enter the body?
7　Who was a good seven feet tall?
8　What did Lister use to open his red letter with?
9　Who didn't like 'wets, weirdos and fatties'?
10　Who had buttered the underside of his tie?
11　Why had Lister kept his adoptive grandmother's false teeth?
12　Why can't Rimmer be frightened?
13　What was Lister's clearance number?
14　Who, in Dr Thompson's opinion, was a grade two sociopath?
15　Who did Rimmer describe as 'a combination of Captain Courageous, the Scarlet Pimpernel and James Bond'?
16　Which company repossessed Rimmer's body?
17　According to Rimmer, who was born with a leak in the think tank?

18 Who saved Lister's life on Lotomi 5?

19 What does Kryten look forward to?

20 Why had 'Lister's' adoptive father been sentenced to ten years in prison?

21 Who was the cop in Bedford Falls?

22 According to Lister, what was he convinced anthems did?

23 For how long had John Ewe been doing the Jovian run?

24 How many traffic-light-coloured striped tank tops hung in Lister's Cyberhell wardrobe?

25 Why did the Cat want to head back to *Red Dwarf*?

26 How much was the original tip that Rimmer gave Lister?

27 What was Valter Holman's sentence?

28 What was 'Kryten's' arm holding in its hand?

29 Who could be outwitted by a contestant from Junior Criss Cross Quiz?

30 What does CLITORIS stand for?

31 According to Kryten, how had *Homo sapiens* reached the top of the evolutionary tree?

32 Who wore an expression that would have blown away Mrs Danvers and Nurse Ratchet in a stern-looks competition?

33 According to Lister, what could you still taste at half past two in the afternoon?

34 Why did Rimmer hate marines?

35 What sort of flower had Lister grown on Garbage World?

36 What colour were the Cyberlake's waters?

37 How many guests were there at the Rimmers' party?

38 Where did Henry apply for a sweeping job?

39 Who partnered Lister when searching for *Starbug*'s engines?

40 What's GOD?

41 For the first time in history, for how long had the commentators been totally speechless?

42 Who had conducted Lister's defence for his trial in the Forum of Justice on Arranguu 12?

43 At what time did the souvenir shop unopen?

44 What did the crew place inside Lister's coffin with him?

45 Who had strutted around *Starbug* 'like a male model from a mail-order cardigan catalogue'?

46 How long did the crew have to take off from the Backwards universe due to planetary conditions?

47 What had happened on 'Black Friday'?

48 In an average fourteen-hour working day, how much hard graft could the Cat be relied upon to put in?

49 Who was the boy behind Rimmer in the two hundred yards dash?

50 What was Rimmer's first new genetic structure?

51 How old was Mozart when he died?

52 What did Rimmer do when he saw a fight start?

53 What nationality was Avril Dupont?

54 Who was 'Vinegar Drawers'?

55 Where was the women's washroom situated aboard *Red Dwarf*?

56 Where had Dr Sabinsky's legs been sent by mistake?

57 What did Lister use to open Kryten's skull?

58 How many times did Lister watch the fast-motion replay of his 'pool' shot?

59 How long had Lister served in Cyberhell?

60 How many days of exploratory digging had it taken Lister to find a thorium lode?

61 Who was Monsieur Chat?

62 Who had brought up a child on a geo-mapper's wages?

63 How high were Trixie LaBouche's stilettos?

64 Who has technology way in advance of the crew's?

65 Where would you find a plastic model of the Vatican, aboard *Red Dwarf*?

66 Whose call sign was 'Jewish cowboy'?

67 Who was educated at Chethams's Hospital School of Music?

68 What had Lister worn for his trial?

69 According to Rimmer, what letters does Kryten have after his name?

70 How many suits were there in the Cat's emergency travel wardrobe?

71 Where had Lister found a jet-powered space bike?

72 How many 'volunteers' had the Dingotangs put on the first ship?

73 What was first on Lister's list of humankind's many magnificent achievements?

74 Where did Cyberhell remind Lister of?

75 Why was 'Big Iron' so called?

76 What colour is destrol fluid?

77 Where was the APR clause located in McIntyre's loan agreement?

78 How many oils of C'fardeert are there?

79 Why was Ernest in prison?

80 Who commanded the Space Corps Research and Development Programme?

81 According to Kryten, if the crew enter the caverns what's their chance of survival?

82 Whose saliva tasted like a cross between a stagnant canal and airline chicken kiev?

83 Where would you find a salmon-tinted Aubusson rug aboard *Red Dwarf*?

84 What colour was the Rage?

85 What was the first and only example of agonoid interior design?

86 Who had stayed at the Hotel Paradiso?

87 Where was the sewage dumped on Garbage World?

88 What colour was the tide-mark left by Kochanski's silver locket?

89 How long had Lister spent in prison for a crime he didn't commit?

90 What was the stigma of the dead?

91 How many times did Rimmer allow the telephone to ring before he answered it?

92 What was Mamie's surname?

93 What was the Forum of Justice built from?

94 What was the 'Ultimate Hallucinogen'?

95 How long had it taken the crew to find canister 1121?

96 Who was *Better Than Life* dedicated to?

97 Who had encouraged Lister to sign up for night classes in mechanics?

98 How many times did the pebbles bounce?

99 Why did the Rage choose Lister's other self?

100 Who was the 'Queen of Panic'?

101 What two things had Rimmer learnt from his etiquette book?

102 How long would it take to attach the landing jets to
      Starbug?

103 Where was Lister serving his sentence?

104 According to Rimmer, what's the trouble with
      democracy?

105 What is the Cartesian Principle?

106 Who found it tough to write and post a letter?

107 How much had Rimmer's and Helen's wedding
      cost?

108 Who was Michael Longman's second assistant?

109 What colour was Dennis McBean's anorak?

110 Who's Cyberhell did Lister enter by mistake?

111 What were Rimmer's last words before he entered
      the Rage?

112 Who overtook Rimmer in class?

113 How had Rimmer escaped from the storage vault?

114 What colour was Kryten's cagoul?

115 How long does the astronavigation exam last?

116 What did John Ewe specialize in?

Staircase 2

When the words listed below are placed horizontally and in the correct order within the grid, they will spell out diagonally (in the boxes marked in bold) another word from *Red Dwarf*.

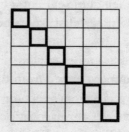

HUDZEN
PADDLE
NORWEB
GUITAR
HECTOR
NODNOL

'What a guy!'
Spanners, 'Dimension Jump'

1 Who was responsible for Ace's nick on the forehead?
2 How had Ace escaped his bonds?
3 Who taught Kryten how to play the piano?
4 Who gave Ace a black eye?
5 How strong was the gale that Ace and Lister ventured into?
6 What did Ace want Rimmer to do after Ace had died?
7 Where did Ace learn field microsurgery?
8 How had Ace died in Dimension 165?
9 According to Ace Rimmer, how had he got his black eye?
10 Whose bed did Ace sit by day after day, night after night?
11 Where had Ace Rimmer spent most of his life?
12 What did Ace tell Lister to do if Rimmer got cold feet?
13 What sends Ace Rimmer into the 'land of nod'?
14 What was Ace Rimmer's only vice?
15 What time was Ace's bash down in the mess?
16 On which side of his forehead did Ace have a small nick?
17 What rank was Ace Rimmer?
18 According to Rimmer, who was Ace 'as butch as'?
19 What did Ace give Spanners as a farewell gift?
20 How long did Ace have to train Rimmer as his replacement?
21 According to Rimmer, who wears women's underwear?
22 How had Ace earned his gold tooth?

23 What was Ace's first love?
24 Where had Ace had his highlights done?

Staircase 3

When the words listed below are placed horizontally and in the correct order within the grid, they will spell out diagonally (in the boxes marked in bold) another word from *Red Dwarf*.

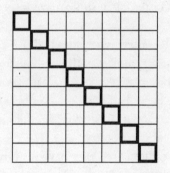

DANDRUFF
SIMULANT
PARALLEL
VALKYRIE
GAZPACHO
LANSTROM
NAPOLEON
BULGARIA

'Dormouse cheeks!'

1 How many counts of 'general insubordination' had Lister been reported for?

2 What was Lister's nickname at school?

3 Which guitar string does Lister use to floss his teeth with?

4 Where had Lister taken shore leave to get over Kochanski?

5 According to Lister, what does he hold a Ph.D. in?

6 What did Lister think was Boyle's fourth law?

7 What had Lister used to make a bath for Kochanski?

8 How many pages had been torn out of Lister's diary?

9 According to Lister, what qualities does he have that elevate him above poultry?

10 Where did millionaire Lister have his private island?

11 Where did Lister want to go for a curry hunt?

12 According to Lister, who did Confidence sound like?

13 What had Lister stolen from a hotel in his youth?

14 How many songs were there in Lister's 'collection'?

15 How many horses was Lister going to have on his farm on Fiji?

16 According to Lister, how do humans recharge?

17 How did Lister get into art college?

18 When did Lister do a 'scout' salute?

19 According to Lister, why couldn't he possibly be gay?

20 How much of Lister's memory did he give Rimmer?

21 Which 'buttock' did Lister burn with his iron?

22 According to Lister, who wore 'child molester' glasses?

23 Why did Lister want his left arm chopped off?

24 Why did Lister leave his job as a supermarket trolley attendant?

25 How long did it take Lister to unbutton his flies with one hand?

26 According to Lister, what could the owner of the 'footprints' go to a fancy dress party as?

27 How did Lister describe Rimmer in court?

28 What was Lister's incentive to obey Rimmer?

29 According to Lister, what was his number one subject at school?

30 Where had Lister stepped out of a packing crate 'bollock naked'?

Word search 3
Non-human life forms

The words listed opposite are 'hidden' in the grid. They may be found written vertically, horizontally or diagonally, and even backwards.

```
A X E K J U C H I P A N A S T E E P H
V P E N O Y T N E D I A M D H M K P P
Q N O I G E L S N E R I S P E G R A R
U R S C A F T C S M U Y I D I E S R O
E X R F A I O N A R A P I L N N T K M
E Q K M L L N E Z O D P G E Q N N A Y
G C I E J E Y E Q F E G G L U Y A Z L
P N N D N Y G P Z E W A R M I M L Z O
E C I E W Q B O S D D J H V S U U I P
E B T S D I O R D E U G O R I T M P A
K P A R X I J S D H B H L B T A I C I
N I W H E B F R N T H O S R O N S V D
H J O S D I O N O G A B Y G R T C E O
U B W A Z I Z C O Y C X E S I H A S C
J E I Q D X A U G C K Z N X D T J R M
D H B S D I O N A H C E M O H A W K O
```

AGONOIDS
APOCALYPSE BOYS
CHIPANASTEE
CONFIDENCE
DEATH
DJUHNKEEP
DOZEN
EMOHAWK
EPIDEME
FAMINE
GELFS
GENNY MUTANT
HUDZEN
KINITAWOWI
LEGION
MAIDENTYONE
MECHANOIDS
PARANOIA
PESTILENCE
PIZZAKRAPP
POLYMORPH
PSIRENS
QUEEG
RENEGADE DROIDS
ROGUE DROIDS
SIMULANTS
THE DEFORMED
THE INQUISITOR
WAR

> **'When I finally get round to writing my Good Psycho Guide, this place is gonna get raves'**
> Lister, 'Legion'

1 What were mechanoids not supposed to have?
2 Where had Lister bought Talkie Toaster?
3 How did Kryten make contact with the nanobots?
4 What is the life expectancy of an Alberog?
5 How does an agonoid get robot-drunk?
6 How many times did the simulant lie?
7 What was a form of greeting to the Snugiraffe?
8 According to Holly, who is Queeg 500?
9 What was in the hillbilly's bed?
10 What was Able's serial number?
11 What did the symbi-morph turn into in order to stop the guards from forcing it into Lister's cell?
12 Why haven't the skutters got any emotions?
13 What was Camille?
14 Why did Kryten name the washing machine?
15 Why hadn't Djuhn 'Keep been attacked by the other agonoids?
16 Who was Brooke Junior's father?
17 Who had dispatched seventy-four of his own crew-mates?
18 What was Kryten and Camille's compatibility factor?
19 How fast can Kryten waddle at top speed?
20 Where would you find a population of mostly pig-based Gelfs?

21 Who had a twin sister called Maxine?

22 Why is it smarter to send Kryten to seek an audience with the Regulator?

23 How long can the rogue simulants keep their subjects alive in a state of perpetual agony?

24 Which member of the crew did the Inquisitor physically kill?

25 How tall was Lister's Gelf bride?

26 How had the nanobots escaped *Red Dwarf*'s scanners?

27 Where were Camille's quarters on board *Red Dwarf*?

28 How many scramble cards did Chi' Panastee have in his head when M'Aiden Ty-One first saw him?

29 Where did the polymorph originate from?

30 Where did the symbi-morph's dart hit Lister?

31 How tall was Lister trying to get 'Albert' to grow?

32 What did Kryten hammer into Talkie Toaster's bread vents?

33 What don't simulants hate?

34 What did all the Blerions wear?

35 According to Lister, why would his marriage to a Kinitawowi never work?

36 What did M'Aiden Ty-One manage to acquire from Chi' Panastee?

37 How did the haddock die?

38 Who's 'red hot' on TV theme tunes?

39 Who were armed with T.27 electron harpoons?

40 Where did the crew meet Hudzen 10 on board *Red Dwarf*?

41 Why had the Gelfs cut the coordinates into four pieces?

42 Who was the computer on board the *Scott Fitzgerald*?

43 What is an emohawk?

44 What would Lister be permitted to spend his last evening with?

45 What did Kryten cut off the Inquisitor's hand with?

46 Who is the symbi–morph's Master?

47 What was Lister's mould called?

48 What was the mechanoid aboard the *Centauri* called?

49 What is the symbi–morph's neutral form?

50 What do nanobots do?

51 According to the skutters, what was the only thing of any substance or beauty in the whole of creation?

52 What had the unbroken symbi–morphs assumed the shape of in order to trap Michael McGruder?

53 What are Rimmer's two options when dealing with the polymorph?

54 What was the Blerions' rope made of?

55 Which species was the Gelf Regulator?

56 How did Camille describe Hammond organ music?

57 What had Kryten named the washing machine?

58 Why had Reketrebn misread Lister's desires?

59 How did Chi' Panastee plan to dispatch the one remaining human?

60 How many psychotic simulants was the prison ship transporting to the penal colony?

61 What did the Kinitawowi tribe do for a living?

62 Which Michael Longman 'creature' stole Kryten's body?

63 How had Karstares died?

64 Who was Leekiel?

65 What did Lister use to try to barter with the Kinitawowi?

66 What did the giant hog wear in bed?

67 How many skutters did Rimmer squash in the piston towers?

68 Why did Kryten repair Talkie Toaster?

69 What is an *Oryctolagus cuniculus*?

70 How long would it take Able to check if he was a 4000 Series?

71 How wide was the Gelf icon?

72 Who had taken over *Red Dwarf* and ripped out Holly?

73 How long did it take the rogue simulants to upgrade *Starbug*?

74 What were the most expensive and complex artificial human substitutes ever created by *Homo sapiens*?

75 Which agonoid spare part was in short supply?

76 How does the Inquisitor ensure that all his victims get a fair hearing?

77 Why had the Gelf S'rtginjum been executed?

78 What was the Despair Squid's defence mechanism?

79 What was an agonoid's definition of a friend?

80 Who did Lister hallucinate in the drive room?

81 How did Kryten stop the Dolochimp from disconnecting the Oblivion virus?

82 What weapon did Kryten try to kill all the crew with while under the influence of the Despair Squid?

83 What makes Kryten and Able brothers?

84 What had the Snugiraffe been created from?

85 Where was the vending machine psiren?

86 Who had masterminded the Death Wheel?

87 At what temperature would the wax droids melt?

88 Which of Lister's goldfish needed repairing?

89 According to Queeg, how long had *Red Dwarf* been going round in circles?

90 Who were 'Pinky and Smeggin' Perky'?
91 How had Epideme left Delta 7?
92 What did the polymorph feed on?
93 Which creatures had the three Michael Longmans been 'modified' with?
94 Why had Kryten's nanobots mutinied?
95 How had the skutters rewired the maintenance decks?
96 What were pleasure Gelfs designed for?
97 When had Lister last seen anything as hideous as the Snugiraffe?
98 How did Holly destroy the Despair Squid?
99 What was Able addicted to?
100 What percentage error margin does Stocky have?
101 What does the Inquisitor do to the wretched?
102 Why didn't skutters believe in Silicon Heaven?
103 How many of his crew-mates had M'Aiden Ty-One cannibalized?
104 How did the Regulator know of Lister's 'crimes'?
105 Where did the crew meet the Inquisitor for the final confrontation?
106 What did Kazwa want Lister to 'volunteer' for?
107 What form did Kryten's psiren take?
108 What species were the Gelf Cyberian guards?
109 Why was the Snugiraffe a prized member of the community?
110 How did Kryten finally kill the psiren?
111 Who was the entire 4000 Series based on?
112 What is the difference between a mechanoid and an agonoid?
113 According to Rimmer, how many buttocks does a Gelf have?

114 Who was Brooke's business rival?
115 When had Kryten's nanobots mutinied and taken over
   Red Dwarf?
116 How old was M'Aiden Ty-One?
117 How many skutters did Lister take mining?
118 Whose intellect was 'awesome'?
119 Where had the nanobots spent the last two years?
120 Which of Hudzen's chips had worn out?
121 In one night, how many times had Talkie Toaster
   interrupted Lister's sleep?
122 What is a polymorph's sixth sense?
123 Where are all Kryten's negative emotions stored?

Crossword 3
'Back to Reality'

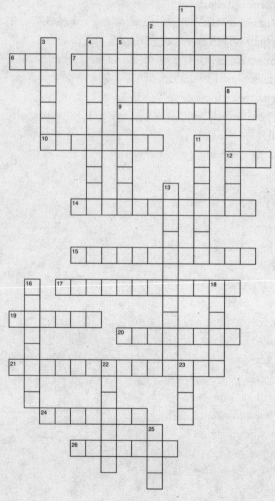

The Questions

Across

2 Jake's surname (6)

6 Sebastian Doyle was Section Chief of this company (1,1,1)

7 *Esperanto*'s weapon (5,6)

9 Duane's overbite (4,5)

10 — of Alteration (8)

12 Despair Squid's venom (3)

14 Company responsible for *Red Dwarf* (7,5)

15 Traffic control (12)

17 Ocean seeding ship (1,1,1,9)

19 Type of mine (6)

20 Billy's cologne? (3,5)

21 Duane's footwear (7,7)

24 Fish similar to this committed suicide (7)

26 Hot drink container! (7)

Down

1 What Duane lacks (4)

2 One of Rimmer's certificates (1,1,1)

3 Mood stabilizer (7)

4 The Despair Squid makes you do this (11)

5 Duane can open these with his overbite (4,7)

8 Half-brothers – same mother (8)

11 Where the Captain's message is hidden (8)

13 Suicidal cephalopod (7,5)

16 Duane's shirt material (3–5)

18 What a bunch of —! (6)

22 Sebastian's rank (7)

23 Brummie git (4)

25 Percentage scored (4)

'Holly, I haven't the slightest clue what you're drivelling about!'
Rimmer, 'White Hole'

State the characters in *Red Dwarf* who said the following, and in which episode.

1 'Rimmer, you already *are* one glorious hole.'
2 'Right, I'll be going then. Going. After all these years, I'll be *going*.'
3 'Go ahead punks, make my day.'
4 'Ah, there, that's it. That's the shape we're looking for, the last chicken in the shop look.'
5 'The way their nostrils flare up like two railway tunnels leading into Snot Street Station.'
6 'Smeg off, dishwasher breath!'
7 'I wonder why anyone would want to name their kid after an airport.'
8 'What toupee?'
9 'If it wasn't for me, he wouldn't even be wearing underpants.'
10 'Key me in, Holly.'
11 'I don't know why I bother, gallivanting off like that, and on our anniversary too.'
12 'Got it, looks like Norman Bates's mum.'
13 'Can't be long, Dave. Hercule has got all the suspects in one room and I'm only two pages away from "also by the same author".'
14 'Let's go, chop, chop. Sorry!'

15 'Ah, Kryten, at last. Glad you could make it this millennium.'

16 'Damn. A flat battery. Who left the lights on?'

17 'Ah, welcome home, son. You've been in all our prayers, you know.'

18 'This is my best top, dammit!'

19 'Is it just me, or is that cockroach shuffling too loudly?'

20 'Ippy dippy, my space shippy. On a course so true. Past Neptune and Pluto's moon. The one I choose is you.'

21 'Come on, stumpy.'

22 'I think we have a suspect.'

23 'He's back, kicking bottom, or what?'

24 'Rimmer, F. I. S. H. That's how you spell fish.'

25 'It's worse than the chronic catarrh sufferers' annual outing.'

26 'Come in number one-six-nine, your time is up.'

27 'Unrumble!'

28 'One week in my body and you've given me a bosom.'

29 'Hold me back, hold me back!'

30 'Boss thinking!'

31 'Just having a little fun, Mr Swanky Pants.'

32 'Quick let's get out of here before they bring him back.'

33 'We love you, A.J.'

34 'So, how did you get to be claustrophobic? Are you born that way, or is it because you're kind of sissy?'

35 'Jim, Bexley, come to Mummy.'

36 'Scum, absolute scum!'

37 'It's also causing a major disturbance in the fabric of my pants!'

38 'Ah, Listy, Listy. Is that a small sewage plant you're carrying in your trousers, or do I detect you're a tad concerned?'

39 'Ask not what your country can do for you, ask what you can do for your country.'

40 'Are you a doctor?'

41 'Smegarama!'

42 'And to compound matters by stealing our ship, it's unbelievably, it's unbelievably . . . naughty.'

43 'Just because some hoity-toity, gonad brain gimp knows an admiral, does he have to broadcast it?'

44 'I'm just popping down the corner shop. Does anyone want anything?'

45 'Hey, wait a minute. I've got it. Don't fish swim south for the winter?'

46 'He's making it up, isn't he? The bloody book doesn't exist.'

47 'They shouldn't bother us then, there's barely a snack on board.'

48 'The truth is in there, that's what turned me into a zombie.'

49 'Well, it's been a few years since I did that.'

50 'Hang on to your wage packet.'

51 'My God, it's me only much more handsome.'

52 'I never want to see or hear from that scum-sucking, lying, weasel-minded smegger in my entire life.'

53 'Indeed, sir, I'm just recovering from the hilarity of the gag myself, almost Swiftian in its rapier-like subtlety.'

54 'So you're saying, Lister, you're an intergalactic pus-filled cold sore?'

55 'I am not having a good day.'

56 'Thy love refreshes and cleanses me like a babbling mountain stream, brother.'

57 'What the hell's happened to my teeth?'

58 'I'm a test pilot in the Space Corps, Bongo. It's my job to do it.'

59 'Oh, make love to me, you horny dude.'

60 'My God, you've got fat, haven't you?'

61 'You can't have been a full member of the golf club, then?'

62 'Is that the firm, delicatessen-bought potato salad, or the squishy gooey stuff in tins?'

63 'Shut up, you dead git!'

64 'My heavens. I'm head head.'

65 'Man, this guy could bore for his country.'

66 'Hey, working-class kid makes good!'

67 'He ain't heavy, sir. He's my brother.'

68 'Come on, give us a snog. I promise I won't try to take off your underpants.'

69 'It's macho but it's not you.'

70 'I just thought I'd give your quarters a quick tickle around, sir.'

71 'What is this, cabaret? Entertainment while you eat?'

72 'To pee or not to pee, that is the question.'

73 'This isn't a meal, it's an autopsy!'

74 'Does anyone else get the feeling we've been led here like lambs to the kebab shop?'

75 'I know what I'm doing, I'm not pished.'

76 'Pity we can't all moon out of the starboard portholes, that always works for me.'

77 'And don't say we're gonna get through this.'

78 'I want a safe, sensible drive, no stunts.'

79 'Well, speaking personally, I hardly didn't get no formal education at all.'

80 'But I could hardly wait six months with a red-hot jape like that under my belt.'

81 'Hey, man. I've only got three legs, will lady pit bull still like me?'

82 'A computer's got to do what a computer's got to do.'

83 'Who disturbs our royal snooze?'

84 'I said I'd be back for breakfast. How are those kippers doing, fellas?'

85 'It's a singularity, a point in the universe where the normal laws of space and time don't apply.'

86 'Not the best news, but it could have been worse.'

87 'Judging by the length of your groinal attachment, you can see why she was so sad to lose him.'

88 'What are you talking about, greasestain?'

89 'Like, erm, why do intelligent people buy cinema hot dogs, you mean that type of weird and mysterious thing?'

90 'It would be like looking for a needle in a male student's flat.'

91 'Don't forget to write, you great nancy.'

92 '*Buon giorno*, give me breakfast.'

93 'Trust me, I know whereof I speak.'

94 'I think our friend the Suicide Squid is about to make an appearance.'

'Purple alert!'
Holly, 'Dimension Jump'

1 What colour was the Cat's crispie bowl?
2 What colour was Jackie Kennedy's suit?
3 What colour was Duane Dibbley's original Thermos?
4 What colour was the writing on the 'alien' pod?
5 What colour was Ace's parachute?
6 What colour were Rimmer's brothers' caps and scarves?
7 What colour was the felt on the grav-pool table?
8 What colour was the ribbon around Lister's 'roast beef'?
9 What colours were the sleeping bags aboard *Red Dwarf*?
10 What colour were Confidence's trousers?
11 What colour were the seats in *Red Dwarf*'s cinema?
12 What colour was Kryten's feather duster?
13 What colour was Mr Flibble's bow-tie?
14 What colour was the pillow in Kochanski's 'bath'?
15 What colour were the headrest covers in the Xpress lift?
16 What colour were the clipboards in the drive room?
17 What colour was the envelope that Rimmer's mother's letter came in?
18 What colour was the cup that Rimmer tested the chicken soup from?
19 What colour were the fluffy dice on *Starbug*?
20 Which colour draughts did Rimmer have?
21 What colour was Lister's knitting?
22 What colour were Kryten's ear-muffs?
23 What colour was Jake Bullet's hatband?

24 What colour was the candle on Rimmer's deathday cake?

25 What colours were the polymorph's bucket and spade?

26 What colour is the Tension Sheet?

27 What colour baseball cap did Petersen wear to George McIntyre's 'welcome back' reception?

28 What colour was Kryten's owner's manual?

29 What colour was Chen's tie?

30 What colour was Rimmer's school blazer and cap?

31 What colour was the luck virus?

32 What colour were the furry dice in Rimmer's E-type Jaguar?

33 What colour was Duane Dibbley's carrier-bag?

34 What colour was the lid of a ship's-issue milk bottle?

35 What colour were the boxer shorts that bend?

36 What colour was Sebastian Doyle's tie?

37 What colour was the Cat's 'magic bag'?

38 What colour were Kochanski's 'ear-muffs'?

39 What colour was Selby's baseball cap at the Nostalgia Night?

40 What colour socks was Rimmer wearing in Kryten's painting?

41 What colour was the future Cat's comb?

42 What colour was the popcorn carton Cat and Lister were eating from when they were watching the black box recording?

43 What colour were Dobbin's drums?

44 What colour was Lister's maintenance trolley?

45 What colour was Lister's passport?

46 What colour were the skutters' dustpan and brush?

47 What colour were the Cat's golfing plus-fours?

48 What colour were the monkey's pants?
49 What colour was the 'old' Lister's cardigan?
50 What colour was Able?
51 What colour were the plumes on the Good Knight's helmet?
52 What colour was Kochanski's tape-measure?

Word search 4
'Would you like some toast?'

The words listed opposite are 'hidden' in the grid. They may be found written vertically, horizontally or diagonally, and even backwards.

BAGELS   GRANARY
BAGUETTES   GRILLED BREAD
BAPS   HOT BUTTERED
BARMCAKES   HOT CROSS BUNS
BREAKFAST SNACK   MUFFINS
BREVILLE   POTATO FARLS
BUNS   PRANDIAL DELIGHTS
CHEESE AND HAM   RAISON D'ETRE
CRAPOLA   SCOTCH PANCAKES
CROISSANTS   TAIWAN
CRUMPETS   TALKIE TOASTER
CURRANT BUNS   TEACAKES
DRY TOAST   TOAST
EARLY MORNING   TOASTED MUFFIN
FARMHOUSE LOAF   WAFFLES
FLAPJACKS

'Novelty condom head!'

1 Why did all of Kryten's heads explode?
2 What will sawing Kryten in half do?
3 According to Kryten, what was the only thing Rimmer was guilty of?
4 What happened when Kryten loosened his adjustment screws?
5 What was Kryten's recall the morning after his 'leaving' party?
6 What does Kryten download his unwanted files into?
7 What did Kryten 'surprise' Lister with?
8 According to Kryten, what qualification has he got?
9 What was Kryten's disguise in the Backwards universe?
10 How does Kryten iron Kochanski's bra?
11 What did Kryten's whole defence case hinge on?
12 Where was Kryten's 'leaving' party held?
13 Why did Kryten want Ace's spare jacket?
14 According to Kryten, who is a 'total dork'?
15 What is the password to the file in Kryten's CPU that he has never been able to access?
16 Who did Kryten describe as 'a piece of sputum floating in the toilet bowl of life'?
17 What had Kryten adapted in order to make the triplicator?
18 What did Kryten use to capture the nanobots?
19 What can Rimmer have Kryten dismantled for?

20 At what time does Kryten need to do an 'emergency dust'?

21 How had Kryten triplicated *Red Dwarf*?

22 Where had Kryten found the matter transporter?

23 When did Kryten wear a dog-collar?

24 How old was Kryten?

25 What did Kryten find in the garbage hold in three thousand separate pieces?

26 Where is Kryten's skull release catch situated?

27 Who did Kryten describe as having 'a Napoleon complex'?

28 What did Kryten study at Toilet University?

29 What is Kryten's security clearance code?

30 What did Spare Head Three claim the others had voted Kryten as?

'This isn't a meal, it's an autopsy!'
Cat, 'Polymorph'

1 What was the drink promoted in Mamie's bar?
2 Where had Kryten caught the lobster?
3 Who was the only man to buy a Topic bar without a hazelnut in it?
4 What shape was Kryten's carrot sculpture?
5 How had all the Indian food supplies been wiped out?
6 Where did Rimmer have breakfast the morning after his stag night?
7 What aperitif did Lister suggest people drink while watching Rimmer's death video?
8 According to Lister, how far is the Cat from the greatest meal of his life?
9 What did Lister's favourite shirt have down the front of it?
10 After four months sober, what was the first thing 'Lister' always vowed he'd do?
11 Who was Henry, originally, going to share his Christmas dinner with?
12 What did the Cat think Lister was going to serve the chicken chasseur in?
13 What did Lister want to do with Rimmer's lemon meringue pie?
14 What were the only two alcoholic beverages left?
15 What were Rimmer's last words before he died?
16 Where was the Marie Lloyd public house situated?

17 What was the Cat's 'food detector'?

18 Which cheese did Hammy prefer?

19 How long was it since Denis had last eaten?

20 What did Lister order in the Better than Life restaurant?

21 What is Kryten's definition of a pub?

22 What had Lister insisted be consumed at his funeral?

23 What had the dispensing machine delivered instead of Lister's customary breakfast?

24 Which was the only night that wasn't curry night?

25 What's Lister's favourite pudding?

26 What did the food dispenser give Lister instead of a black coffee?

27 What presents did the Cat bring Lister on his sick-bed?

28 How long had Lister, Cat and Kryten been on a sprout diet?

29 Who had tried to suffocate himself to death with an onion sandwich?

30 What were the only Liquorice Allsorts left?

31 What was in Mr Capote's 'welcome pack'?

32 What did Lister serve the onion salads in?

33 What had the chocolate dispensers ejected?

34 According to Talkie Toaster, when did Lister last have any toast?

35 What was the range on Lister's curry thermometer?

36 What was Lister's first drink in Cyberhell?

37 According to Lister, how could they get their scrambling time down to one hour sixteen?

38 What was the menu on curry night?

39 According to Lister, what was the dog food?

40 Who were going to wear cardboard hats with humorous arrows through them?

41 What was Petersen drinking aboard the shuttle to *Red Dwarf*?

42 Why had the crew only got one After Eight mint left?

43 Who knows her cheeses?

44 Who drinks Cinzano Bianco?

45 Who did Elvis have a gateau-eating competition with?

46 What did Lister serve the lemon juice with?

47 What sort of wine does Kryten serve with lobster?

48 According to Holly, if Rimmer had been a postman, what shape would his deathday cake have been?

49 What colour was the wine chilling in the ice cooler?

50 What did Kryten pour all over Lister's pizza?

51 Who used to eat his food in alphabetical order?

52 According to Lister, who were 'two lettuces short of an allotment'?

53 What was fossilized between pages 42 and 43 of *How to Get Your Life Together*?

54 How many take-away curries did Lister want to order?

55 What colour were the hats in the Hot Dog and Doughnut Diner supposed to be?

56 What punishment did Lister get for serving Rimmer the 'freaky fungus'?

57 At what time did Bailey's Perfect Shami Kebab Emporium close for the day?

58 According to the Cat, what flavour toothpaste did the Dog use?

59 What sort of cottage cheese did Kochanski say she needed?

60 What was the emergency back-up milk supply?

61 What snack did the Armenian sailor enjoy?

62 What did Lady Sabrina Mulholland-Jjones have for
dinner?

63 Why had Lister given up eating spicy food?

64 What was wrong with Rimmer's dumplings?

65 Who's got 'less backbone than custard'?

66 What had Spare Head Two cooked for breakfast?

67 What did Kryten suddenly feel the need to do when he
was drunk?

68 How long would the skutters watch the lamb?

69 How long had Kryten spent preparing the lobster?

70 Where did Rimmer find the tin of dog food?

71 How many eggs did Lister fry, without breaking a single
yolk?

72 What do you use as a mallet in a game of unicycle
polo?

73 What did Lister offer the giant cockroach?

74 How many lobsters did Kryten get and where did he get
them from?

75 How long was the lifespan of the triplicated
strawberries?

76 How many rounds of toast did the toaster force the Cat
to eat?

77 How many fish did Rimmer bribe the Cat with?

78 Which pizza house did Lister think Kryten had been to?

79 What was Auto Serve's dispensing machines' advertising
slogan?

80 Where were Lister and the Cat situated in the Better
than Life restaurant?

81 For how many days had Lister not eaten before he ate
the dog food?

82 According to Kryten, why did Lister look at Kochanski like a starving man would look at a packet of roasted peanuts?

83 What were Kryten and Camille eating in the cinema?

84 After going into a wine bar, what did Lister fear he could have been doing every Tuesday night?

85 What was Lister's first meal on Backwards world?

86 What did the crew try to change Lister's mutton vindaloo into?

87 What was in the 'lows' fridge?

88 Why does dog's milk last longer than any other kind of milk?

89 What did Mr Darcy think Jane wouldn't enjoy?

90 According to Lister, what effect do sprouts have on him?

91 What ate the last of the corn supply?

92 Who was Bhindy Bhajee really?

93 What flavour was Lister's dog food?

94 Where does Kryten want the salad cream kept?

95 When did the Cat drink Tunisian whisky?

96 Who was Tarka Dhal really?

97 Who made love on a box of tinned asparagus?

98 According to Lister, who was two meals away from being a Sumo wrestler?

99 Where did Lister hide his strawberry and cream waffles?

100 Who is not a cartoonivore?

101 What did Lister have to accompany his sausage and onion gravy sandwich?

102 According to Kryten, how does Kochanski look at Lister?

Staircase 4

When the words listed below are placed horizontally and in the correct order within the grid, they will spell out diagonally (in the boxes marked in bold) another word from *Red Dwarf*.

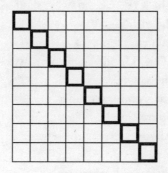

BONEHEAD
REVERSES
CALLISTO
HOLOSHIP
COMPUTER
PIPELINE
GOALPOST
PARANOIA

'Well, forget it, Lister.
Not if you were the last man alive'
Kochanski, 'Epideme'

Identify the episodes by their first and last lines, and also who said the lines.

1 'Arnold. ARNOLD!'
   'It's Wednesday night. It's Amateur Hammond Organ
   Recital Night. OK, take it away, skutters.'
2 'Where is the girl?'
   'Yeah, good luck, man.'
3 'OK, OK, OK. Uphill, slight burrow to the left.'
   'What was he saying?'
4 'Stand by, she's coming round.'
   'This guy's pure class.'
5 'All right. Anyone serving, or what?'
   'I'll see you, son.'
6 '140,000 rehydratable chickens.'
   'How did I do, Mr Lister, sir?'
7 'OK, Rimmer, make this quick.'
   'GO AWAY!!'
8 'Amazing, the last strawberry in the universe.'
   'Boy, this is going to be fun.'
9 'Gentlemen, thank you for attending the meeting.'
   'Speak, Kryten, how can we change what's happening?'
10 'Nineteen. When you are alone in bed, what do you wear?'
   'And the moral of the story is, "Appreciate what you
   got because basically I'm fantastic".'

11 'Cat?'
   'Don't ask!'
12 'Oh, Marnie.'
   'I cannot believe I just said that.'
13 'Holly, give me access to the crew's confidential
   reports.'
   'It's a smegging garbage pod!'
14 'Ten o'clock change-over. Anything to report?'
   'It does work!'
15 'Danger! Do not attempt to open this pod!'
   'If I don't get into some co-ordinated evening wear, I'm
   going to have to resign my post as the most handsome
   guy on the ship!'
16 'Good morning, sir. How about a little breakfast?'
   'Sigmund Freud, eat your heart out.'
17 'Well, that's finished the tests, sir.'
   'Yeah, where am I? No.'
18 'How are you feeling, Mr Lister?'
   'Thank God for that.'
19 'So there we were, two thirty in the morning. I was
   beginning to wish I'd never come to Cadet Training
   School.'
   'Does anyone fancy a vindaloo?'
20 'What is that thing?'
   'Germs.'
21 'Mr Rimmer, sir. We've located the black box terminal,
   you should be getting something now.'
   'We're on our way, sir.'
22 'Ninety-two degrees. God.'
   'Hununga.'
23 'Turn, there's another one.'

'Just one night, I promise. You can have it back first
thing tomorrow, maybe Thursday.'

24 'Ah, let me see. *Astronavigation* and *Invisible Numbers* and
Engineering Made Simple. That's Rimmer's!'
'Souper!'

25 'Thomas Allman. Thomas Allman, you have been found
unworthy of having existed.'
'Give you five? I can do better than that, I can give you
fifteen.'

26 'We're grooving tonight. Ahead, groove factor five,
yeah!'
'OK, that's it. Let's go and erase our memories.'

27 'Mmm, smells good, Kryten. What is it?'
'Don't worry, sir. I'll work on it.'

28 'Oh Jim, aren't you the one who said we have to seize
our moments because they may never come again?'
'Nice to be here Mr Rimmer, you son of a gun!'

29 'Hello, can you hear me?'
'In which case, Mr Rimmer, sir, I should like to take
this opportunity of saying you are the most obnoxious,
trumped-up, farty little smeghead it has ever been my
misfortune to encounter.'

30 'Remain calm, Kryten. This is your CPU speaking.
There has been an accident.'
'No!'

31 'Who the hell are you?'
'Well, let's see what's in there.'

32 'OK, let's try again. What is it?'
'Kryten, this could be the start of a beautiful friendship.'

33 'To Ganymede and Titan, yes sir, I've been around.'
'Look out Earth, the slime's coming home!'

34 'Abandon ship! Abandon ship! Black hole approaching!
This is not a drill. This is a drill . . .'
'We're going to do to Lister what Alexander the Great
once did to me!'

35 'Scramble! Scramble! All hands on deck, emergency
drill. Scramble!'
'What a Dibbley!'

36 'Gravity, one point five. Wind, forty knots and variable.
Coordinates locked and set. Launch scouter.'
'We're here to entertain ya.'

37 'For mild stomach upset, take one teaspoonful. For
acute indigestion, take two.'
'Now, where's those little thumbies?'

38 'Breakfast is served, sir.'
'No silicon heaven? Preposterous. Well, where would
all the calculators go?'

39 'Hello, testing, one two three. Hello.'
'Smeg, I forgot to ask if there were any curry houses in
Dallas.'

40 '. . . lived an old plutonium miner and his daughter,
Clementine.'
'Oh, stop crying and say cheese, boys!'

41 'Maybe it's the moonlight, but I've got to admit, you're
looking pretty good for a corpse.'
'Yeee haaa!!!'

42 'Last week on *Red Dwarf*.'
'Er, guys, we got a problem.'

43 'When I saw you for the first time (first time), my knees
began to quiver (quiver) . . .'
'I'm going to be an uncle!'

44 'Sit down, Brooke. There's something I must tell you.'
'Swivel on it, punk!'

Crossword 4
'Dimension Jump'

The Questions

Across

2 He offered to be covered in taramasalata (5)
4 This may cover Melly! (5,5)
11 Film Lister claimed to be going to see (4)
12 Ace's job (4,5)
13 Ace would be back for this! (9)
15 Spanners (7)
16 Ace's computer needed a stiff upper one (5)

Down

1 Where *Starbug* crashed (5,6)
3 Ace suffered this (6,3)
5 What a guy! (3)
6 Where the 'classic wines' came from (7)
7 Kind of dance Rimmer is fond of (6)
8 Where Lister used to go fishing (5)
9 She resigned! (5)
10 '—— *in Boots*' (magazine) (3,4)
14 Type of alert Holly put the crew on (6)

'Shakespeare? Who's Shakespeare?'
Lister, 'Waiting for God'

State which character said the following, and in which
Red Dwarf novel.

1 'What the smeg is happening, you dough-brained streak
   of venereal pus!'
2 'Follow that coffin.'
3 'I remember . . . something about onions.'
4 'You're a hideous emotional cripple, and you know it.'
5 'He does a lot of lurking, sir.'
6 'Baby, my stick work is *always* great.'
7 'Hann abe kh nik nitre khp. (No wedding, no deal.)'
8 'Ah, Listy. So glad you could tear yourself away from
   your imaginary friends and join us.'
9 'Can't be done, me old buckeroo. Your number is up.'
10 'Come on, you flab-tittied slag.'
11 'I hate killing people. It's such a downer.'
12 'Now, did you manage to dig the black box out, you
   old tartlet?'
13 'Whatever you do, don't access reality – you're not
   going to like it one little bit.'
14 'Essential to the project? What do you do, use his breath
   for fuel?'
15 'It was a *mano a mano*, ninja-type struggle, where a
   brave, rather ruggedly handsome red kitchen appliance
   finally managed to come out on top.'

16 'I think he said, "We can relax. My suits are safe."'
17 'Then you can bend me over the desk and give me a damned good spanking, OK?'
18 'She nearly pulled the damned thing off.'
19 'One good rump grunt from Lister's curry-fevered backside would blast me out of existence.'
20 'That was a heck of a night. One heck of a night.'
21 'Down Crap Creek, Rimmer. Without a paddle or a smegging boat.'
22 'So you say. All the same, I'd feel slightly more comfortable if we weren't actually overtaking radio waves.'
23 'You've got to get them out of here. I don't know how long I can plug this gap.'
24 'I have no particular plans for the rest of this reality.'
25 'How's your verruca these days?'
26 'Don't you think that was perhaps a teeny, tiny taddette irresponsible?'
27 'My curiosity was piqued, man. Who the hell *are* you?'
28 'Look out, planet Earth, sex god alert!'
29 'I'll rip out its windpipe and whip it to death with the tonsil end.'
30 'You're absolutely right, Duke.'
31 'Hey – What d'you expect for $£19.99 plus tax? Conversation, quantum theory *and* good toast?'
32 'I'd hate to have gone knowing your panties were still crinkled.'
33 'That's comedy! That is comedy!'
34 'Well, that's our Listy all right. Discreet, isn't he? The last thirty-odd years seem to have mellowed him out completely.'

35 'I said: the bad–assed robot dude who grabbed you has gotten hold of the guy who looks like goalpost head . . .'

36 'The question is, do we want to?'

37 'My ass is prettier than my face! When we get back, I'm gonna have them surgically swapped.'

38 'Sorry, bud, I just lost my grip.'

39 'I'm from Sidcup. I'm an engineer.'

40 'We don't even have the technology to keep out a bandy-legged, brain-dead hillbilly with a gene pool no bigger than a spider's piss puddle.'

41 'Perhaps you'd like me to run down to Supplies and buy you some more.'

42 'We're home.'

43 'Shoot the ugly goitre-faced gimboid!'

44 'Are you going to blow the whole deal just because she doesn't hit your G-spot?'

45 'You're pretty gosh-darn out of your smegging tree, Rimmer.'

46 'I've got some bad news, Frank. You'd better sit down.'

'There's an old human saying – If you're going to talk garbage, expect pain'
Rimmer, 'Emohawk – Polymorph II'

State the characters in *Red Dwarf* who said the following, and in which episode.

1 'What the hell, it's for a good cause.'
2 'I'm so ugly, I never get invited to parties.'
3 'So is it a simple registry office or a full church do for you two?'
4 'From now on, call me Tiger.'
5 'Of course we have. It's the cockpit, dummy. We come here all the time.'
6 'Hey, it hasn't happened has it, it has will have going to happen happened but hasn't actually happen happened yet, h'actually!'
7 'That was no accident, that was first degree toastercide.'
8 'That was Ace Rimmer. We're lucky to be alive.'
9 'I suppose, in many ways, I should have updated the system really.'
10 'I'm gonna die! I've been fished to death!'
11 'Smeg, Outland Revenue!'
12 'Stand aside, let the law handle this.'
13 'Sorry to gooseberry, Kryten, but we've got a visitor down in the hangar.'
14 'Hey, Dave, what's this? The Christmas special?'
15 'Farewell, brother. My brook is babbled.'

16 'Just call me Badass!'

17 'Better grab a brolly, there's a bit of a drizzle outside.'

18 'I was thinking it might help pass the time if I created a perfectly functioning replica of a woman.'

19 'So we did plant a bomb, I was beginning to wonder.'

20 'Well, I want to talk to you about my penis.'

21 'Woah! Crease!'

22 'He's not Dave, he's the anti-Lister.'

23 'Yes, of course it is, bozo!'

24 'It's like water roaring down, say a passageway, in a kind of roaring, watery, kind of way. I wonder what the hell it is?'

25 'But you do sound like you eat a lot of curries.'

26 'Urgh! To think I caressed his pod!'

27 'Cor, what a bunch of twonks.'

28 'Is now a good time to ask about a pay rise?'

29 'The Browns are going to have to do something quite sensational with their last bubble. Quiet please.'

30 'I think I've reached the age now when I really should be wearing clogs.'

31 'Is he totally perfect, or what?'

32 'This place is harder to get into than airline chicken kiev.'

33 'Sometimes you astonish even me.'

34 'How do you want yours, permed or blow-dried?'

35 'What, and spoil your tea?'

36 'Wibbley thing or swirly thing and he refuses to commit himself. He's losing it, he really is.'

37 'Did you see him clearly? Did you get a good look at his face? Could you spot him in a parade? I don't think so. I could have been anybody.'

38 'It's because of her, isn't it? She who must be drooled over.'

39 'Cat, when I get you I'm going to turn you into a kebab.'

40 'I can't believe you're here. How did you persuade Kryten to let you out?'

41 'Dave, why didn't you just tell me how you felt about me when I was still alive?'

42 'By God, we'll rescue these fair blooms or my name's not Captain A. J. Rimmer, Space Adventurer.'

43 'It's better to live one hour as a tiger than a whole lifetime as a worm.'

44 'I have a medium-sized fire axe buried in my spinal column, sir.'

45 'What use are they? It's like giving Blind Pugh contact lenses.'

46 'Oh my God, Caroline. You've really let yourself go.'

47 'Go on, he's probably picked a ring.'

48 'My father was a jellybrain!'

49 'Well, that's what people say, but where's the evidence?'

50 'Maybe it's tot, I don't know. But it's funny, even to this day I can't look at a pair of nutcrackers without wincing.'

51 'I'm just doing my job, it's not my fault that I love it.'

52 'Don't get your double helix in a straight. No one's questioning your nasal integrity.'

53 'What is wrong with that demented Tonka toy now?'

54 'Wait a minute, I never used to be a man.'

55 'Anyway, they did that word that I can't say to the whole ship and left all the bits they didn't want on that planetoid.'

56 'Stick to your usual type, women with little wispy
beards who wear three overcoats and carry little bags full
of string.'

57 'Will people not leave it in here, it just makes us look as
if we don't know what the hell we're doing.'

58 'You wanted driving, I'm driving you.'

59 'Emergency! Emergency! There's an emergency going
on!'

60 'Just don't get caught or I'm out cold for six months,
OK?'

61 'Rasputin, I'm very cross indeed.'

62 'This is worse than playing away at Leeds.'

63 'I didn't ask to be killed, Lister. Life's a bitch, now smeg
off, I'm busy.'

64 'Eureka! I've done it!'

65 'Dave Lister, the man with the galaxy-sized jockstrap.'

66 'Has anyone ever told you that you are a disgusting,
pus-filled bubo who has all the wit, charm and self-
possession of an Alsatian dog after a head-swap
operation?'

67 'Actually, we know sod all about space travel, but if
you've got a blocked nozzle, we're your lads.'

68 'Better anything than that toupee.'

69 'Hey, Bent Bob, how's it going mate?'

70 'OK, keep 'em peeled, guys.'

71 'Do I have a head shaped like an amusing ice cube?'

72 'It's gonna be a cold day in hell before I touch barbecue
wings again.'

73 'That'll teach you to be bread baskets.'

74 'Welcome to the Rimmer Experience, a place of
wonder, excitement and . . . wonder.'

75 'I say let's get into the jet-powered rocket pants and junior birdman the hell out of here.'

76 'Don't be alarmed, sir. But I have a very strange tale to tell.'

77 'I'll just have the toast.'

78 'There's enough fried calamari out there to feed the whole of Italy.'

79 'Did someone just turn over two pages at once?'

80 'You may as well marry a box of Daz.'

81 'This nut's not for cracking.'

82 'Oh my goodness, it's Princess Leia.'

83 'Nice-looking bloke.'

84 'Oh, vomitization! I don't believe it!'

85 'Ignore him. He's a complete and total nutter, and he's only got one testicle.'

86 'It's an obscene phone call, sir. I think it's for you.'

87 'Ah, you're a waffle man.'

88 'Oh yes. Totty, totty, totty.'

89 'It's just a dream. Thank God for that. Just a dream.'

90 'I'm an animal. I'm a tasteless, uncouth, mindless, tone-deaf, randy, blokish, semi-literate space bum.'

91 'Is it me, or has it suddenly got rather hot in here?'

92 'That many!?'

93 'Excuse me, sir, but a gentleman appears to have appeared in the corner of the room.'

94 'It's so damn hot I can barely breathe. It's like being stuck in a sauna with a fat man on your face.'

Word search 5
Episodes

The episode titles listed opposite are 'hidden' in the grid below. They may be found written vertically, horizontally or diagonally, and even backwards. Titles of two or more words may be hidden in different parts of the grid.

```
R D P A Y P N P M O X T H E L A S T D A Y V E N Z Y O V D V
M E T T T A T I M E S L I D E S H K E G E A Z F F Z K O N X
C M P T H R D L O U W U X X R E A W A N D P A R A N O I A G
L O M P E A T E O U J A E A A K O A D H I G U N M E N O F D
Q N G D I L N W N X R N H P Y O R H O X R T A O V E M I C Y
E S Z F N L R K D O J O O X Y J H O G W O R N Y S K R N O O
N A X F Q E C C S Q O C B I K A R M R F T U A A B T A H N H
P N T M U L Q A N F A R B O S D Y E O G A H T A R N C D F D
E D P L I U S T E L O X A V R N W C F P K E P O A A L U I H
H A B Z S N T E Y M E R C M R O E A G B K O L R F R U E D O
H N N Z I I A P O O E X K M P Y S M N P I V C O O T Y Q E L
R G U M T V S N C H S K T F S E G I I R T H F W H M I Y N O
A E R Y O E I I U Z C Y O D P B L L T D Y M R E X E Y M C S
M L E N R R S B E T T E R T H A N L I F E E M R W L T L E H
P S M E M S L J K H C A E D S K U E A Q M E B G Y T X I O I
A B E T H E E N D N W Y A R Q X G Y W M M Q B C A D C H H P
B O D Y S W A P A K W K L G U L E G I O N I Z K R O P Y Y W
N Y I R R L K L C Q Y F I Z T T E R R O R F O R M W A F N J
F B P K J A A A P J U S T I C E U Y X S P S I R E N S F H W
P H E C J B B P A W Z R Y U T F Q F B K H P R O M Y L O P L
```

THE END

FUTURE ECHOES

BALANCE OF POWER

WAITING FOR GOD

CONFIDENCE AND
  PARANOIA

ME[2]

KRYTEN

BETTER THAN LIFE

THANKS FOR THE
  MEMORY

STASIS LEAK

QUEEG

PARALLEL
  UNIVERSE

BACKWARDS

MAROONED

POLYMORPH

BODYSWAP

TIMESLIDES

THE LAST DAY

CAMILLE

DNA

JUSTICE

WHITE HOLE

DIMENSION JUMP

MELTDOWN

HOLOSHIP

THE INQUISITOR

TERRORFORM

QUARANTINE

DEMONS AND
  ANGELS

BACK TO REALITY

PSIRENS

LEGION

GUNMEN OF THE
  APOCALYPSE

EMOHAWK –
  POLYMORPH
  TWO

RIMMERWORLD

OUT OF TIME

TIKKA TO RIDE

STOKE ME A
  CLIPPER

OUROBOROS

DUCT SOUP

BLUE

BEYOND A JOKE

EPIDEME

NANARCHY

'Goalpost head!'

1 What was Rimmer doing in the drive room at the time of the accident?
2 According to the Cat, what were Rimmer's good qualities?
3 According to Rimmer, who was Adolf Hitler?
4 Why did Rimmer use only three pieces of toilet paper?
5 According to Rimmer, what did Scott hit Captain Oates over the head with?
6 What was Rimmer's IQ rating?
7 What did Rimmer wear with his red-and-white checked gingham dress?
8 According to Rimmer, what makes us different from animals?
9 Why had Rimmer named all his shoe trees?
10 According to Rimmer, who was responsible for losing *Red Dwarf*?
11 Who did Rimmer describe as a 'brummie git'?
12 Who was Rimmer's 'widow'?
13 What did Rimmer do to get eight weeks PD?
14 Who's got more balls than Rimmer?
15 According to Rimmer, who said 'I am what I am'?
16 Where had Rimmer been decorated and used as a Christmas tree in the town square?
17 At what time was Rimmer playing Risk at Cadet Training School?

18 What did Rimmer's sister-in-law do for a living?

19 According to Rimmer, at what age do you suddenly become a 'fat bastard'?

20 How old was Rimmer when he went on a school trip to Macedonia?

21 What had Rimmer been researching while Ace was away?

22 What did Rimmer sing while searching for the polymorph?

23 How old was Rimmer when he went on his survival course with the Space Scouts?

24 According to Lister, what was one of Rimmer's redeeming features?

25 Where was Rimmer going to have 'an humiliating panic attack'?

26 What did Rimmer compare the quality of *Blue Midget*'s visual monitor to?

27 According to Lister, why can't you confuse Rimmer with a book?

28 Who threw Rimmer's animal track shoes into a septic tank?

29 What had Rimmer done to Stinky Bateman's turn-ups in third-form prep?

30 Who did Rimmer attack, thinking they were giraffes that were armed and dangerous?

31 What does Rimmer do at the first sign of danger?

Word search 6
The Rimmer Experience

The words highlighted in the song opposite are 'hidden' in the grid. They may be found written vertically, horizontally or diagonally, and even backwards.

```
R Y F M A S T E R Z P O A P F
F E A R L E S S M E D Z E G D
H A N D S O M E E J M I G H T
H E T N F Q E V S L I M M E R
K H A S Y R A E M I S S I O N
G G S D I R E C T I V E S R T
U L T O B R B L O R H L T E G
C N I U O H R L I M A A A O B
G O C M O T I J U A M P K I A
L S Y A M H G B S Y B A E R J
J J U Y N E T T D T H L N R U
X D E R N N R I P O B O E D N
C W Y I F A Y Y W U L M V E E
E N U G Y H H O D M A E N I
X S R H Y S A R B I L D R R U
U D R T P T T R R N O U A J C
W P L A Y G D T D N J X O Y S
O M C A R D S Q T E X X T W Y
O E C J B W R C Q R N J I R F
C O K L I F E I B H O T Z L V
N O L M M X M V A O S U C H N
W I M S M S M N A K Y A N X M
W E L E R I I R U S Z Z Q D N
R U N E U K R T W T K L U B B
P V C T P A C T T C Y H Q L I
```

The Questions

If you're in **trouble**, he **will save** the **day**
He's **brave** and he's **fearless**, come **what may**
Without him the **mission** would **go astray**
He's **Arnold**, Arnold, Arnold **Rimmer**
Without him **life would** be much **grimmer**
He's **handsome**, **trim** and no one's **slimmer**
He will never **need** a Zimmer

He's Arnold, Arnold, Arnold Rimmer
More reliable than a **garden strimmer**
He's never been **mistaken** for **Yul Brynner**
He's not **bald** and his **head** doesn't **glimmer**

Master of **wit** and the **repartee**
His **command** of **space directives** is **uncanny**
How come he's **such** a **genius**? **Don't** ask me

Ask Arnold, Arnold, Arnold Rimmer
He's **also** a **fantastic swimmer**
And if you **play** your **cards right**, then he just **might**
Come round for **dinner**

'It took me ages to mark these cards!'
Lister, 'Bodyswap'

1 What is Lister's favourite 3-D video game?
2 Which movie has Kryten seen a thousand times?
3 Who woke up with an orange-and-white striped traffic cone in his bed after Rimmer's stag night?
4 How long had the crew intended to go fishing for?
5 What colour was Dick's 'big ball'?
6 What was one of the most popular pub games of the 20th century?
7 How long had the crew been playing 'Red Dwarf'?
8 According to Kryten, what is it that makes Lister happy in bed?
9 How many consecutive games of pool had Lister won in the Aigburth Arms, and how long had it taken him?
10 What had Rimmer 'won' the last time he played the locker room game?
11 What 'dance' did Lister and Confidence do outside *Red Dwarf*?
12 Where did Lister used to go condom fishing?
13 How many Mental–metal hardrock discs were there in 'Lister's' collection?
14 What was the objective of playing 'Red Dwarf' for Lister?
15 Who's winning in Holly's postal chess game?
16 Which film was usually playing at the movie houses on Cyberhell?

17 What 'party' did Rimmer and his stag night guests gatecrash?

18 What par was Kryten's fifteen-mile golf hole?

19 What had Lister been watching when he was plucked out of Cyberhell?

20 According to Kryten, who would never get on the cover of *Vogue*?

21 According to *Up, Up and Away*, which country has been the home of some of the most remarkable weaving to come out of north-west Europe?

22 Which channel screened *Tales of the Unexpected*?

23 Who had trained in jujitsu and judo for five years?

24 Who played the banjo?

25 According to Rimmer, if Lister's shirt was a cat book, what would it be?

26 How many boys took part in the Junior B's two hundred yards dash?

27 Which musical instrument does Billy Bailey play?

28 How long had Lister had his authentic Les Paul copy guitar?

29 Who had Esperanto classes from the age of six?

30 How long had Kryten spent reading *Big Iron at Sun-up*?

31 Where did Kryten borrow the T72 from?

32 Who did the alternative Rimmer let win the two hundred yards dash?

33 What did Rimmer say would kill a couple of centuries while Lister was in stasis?

34 Why did Lister claim that he, Cat and Kryten didn't invite Rimmer on the fishing holiday?

35 What night of the week was Nostalgia Night held on?

36 How many times had Rimmer been round the planetoid looking for his golf ball?

37 What did Confidence think was the greatest love song ever written?

38 How had Kryten compiled the exhibits in the Rimmer Experience?

39 For which age group was the Cat's book that Lister was reading intended for?

40 Whose sports kit did Rimmer wear for the Junior B's two hundred yards dash?

41 When Rimmer and Lister were playing golf on the planetoid, where did Lister's ball go?

42 How many extra points do you get for not breaking your bubble?

43 According to Deb Lister, who wrote *Hamlet*?

44 Which tune did Lister's musical toilet-roll holder play?

45 Which soap was produced by Groovy Channel 27?

46 What was Lister's favourite carol?

47 What did Gordon describe as the 'little knobbly ones down the front'?

48 What size golf course had Kryten built on the planetoid?

49 If wrongosity ever became an Olympic sport, who could represent his species?

50 What are the competitors in a game of Toot?

51 How many brushes do you get with your Portable Walrus Polishing Kit?

52 What was Kryten's definition of fun?

53 Who won the two hundred yards dash?

54 How many G strings were there on Lister's guitar?

55 How many consecutive games of chess had Holly lost to Talkie Toaster?

56 What do you use as a net in a game of Durex volleyball?

57 When did Rimmer want to 'book' Lister's body for?

58 Which radio station did Kryten want to pick up on his nipple?

59 How far did Scotland get in the 2224 World Cup?

60 Who wrote *Big Iron at Sun-up*?

61 How many *Red Dwarf* TIV machines were there?

62 What video did Lister find in Locker 68?

63 According to Lister, what was showing as the midnight movie?

64 Who can stay awake during operas?

65 What is Kryten's favourite dream?

66 What was the health warning that came with Rasta Billy Skank?

67 What had Captain Richards been doing when the steering system went doolally?

68 What does Lister think is more melodious than Reggie Wilson?

69 What did Rimmer imagine when he decided he wanted to win the two hundred yards dash?

70 Why did the Cat invite Kryten to join in the weekly crap game?

71 Which locker had Lister opened, and what had he won?

72 Where would you find tables for cuarango and flip?

73 How did Kryten ration his reading of *Big Iron at Sun-up*?

Crossword 5
'Tikka to Ride'

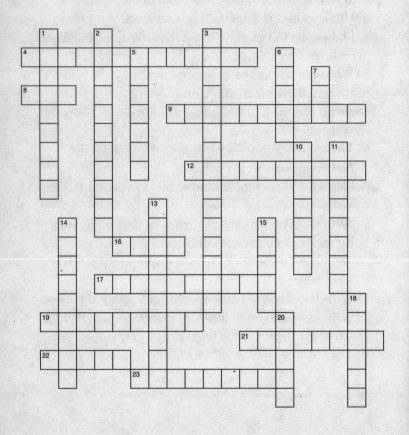

The Questions

Across

4 The President's wife (6,7)

8 You bet your —! (3)

9 Where the second gunman was (6,5)

12 This was roasted! (4,6)

16 The crew came back from this! (4)

17 Where Oswald originally fired from (5,5)

19 Used to travel in time (4,5)

21 J.F.K. Airport, formerly (8)

22 — Bookstore Depository (5)

23 What Kryten downloaded (4,5)

Down

1 Lister ignored this! (9)

2 The number of vindaloos Lister wanted to order (4,7)

3 Assassin (3,6,6)

5 Identity of the second gunman (7)

6 What Spare Head Two does, which Kryten does not (5)

7 Spare Head — (3)

10 Kind of socket Kryten has (7)

11 The month in which Kennedy was killed (8)

13 What Lister thought was on the pavement (5,5)

14 What must not be altered (4,5)

15 What Lister was hunting for (5)

18 American city (6)

20 The Cat needed to do this after eating (5)

'Excuse me, Voter Colonel – but is this some kind of test?'
Cop, 'Back to Reality'

1 What is it about Lister that makes Rimmer want to puke?
2 Whose mouth is a 'skuttle-free zone'?
3 What happens to naughty boys who have been naughty?
4 Which universal dilemma has confronted all men since the beginning of time?
5 Who moved pawn to queen five?
6 What was Princess Bonjella's Christian name?
7 What was the name of the town that Rimmer thought might be named after Lister and Kryten?
8 When was the last time Lister had tried to urinate on top of Rimmer from the top of D deck?
9 What equipment was not allowed in the engineering exam?
10 According to Kryten, why do guys have nostril hair?
11 Where did Kryten and Lister materialize when they should have appeared by the navi-comp on *Starbug*?
12 What did Rimmer try to learn 'while he slept'?
13 Who is a heavy sleeper?
14 Who did Humphrey Bogart lie to in *Casablanca*?
15 What command did Lister have to type in to erase the novels of Agatha Christie?
16 When was the first siphon and valve flushing system patented?
17 What is impossible to do in the Justice Zone?

18 Where was it written that 'the iron shall lie down with the lamp'?

19 By how much had *Starbug*'s cargo deck expanded?

20 What was item 34 on Rimmer's daily goal list?

21 Where was the Captain's message hidden?

22 According to Lister, why couldn't Rimmer become the next Ace?

23 According to Rimmer, what did the Eskimos do with their elderly?

24 Whose name was on the cryogenic escape pod?

25 To what did Lister accredit Rimmer being such a good singer?

26 Whose sleeping quarters are situated next to the sewage processor?

27 What were the contents of Adolf Hitler's briefcase?

28 Where did the USSR install a nuclear base in return for Mafia cocaine trafficking between Cuba and the States?

29 Who thought Jesus was a hippie?

30 Who were like 'the funny walk in cystitis'?

31 According to Kochanski, when had Lister last had a bath?

32 Who took Rimmer and Kryten prisoner?

33 What was the reason for Lister's 'mutiny'?

34 Who was on 24-hour wipe alert?

35 In which episode did Rimmer become an officer?

36 How long had the Srehtorb Esrever Lanoitasnes Eht been working at the Nogard dna Egroeg?

37 Which supply pipe had the Cat entered to reach the cargo decks?

38 Who was the 'knight' searching for aboard *Starbug*?

39 How much had Rimmer borrowed from Lister to buy his birthday present?

40 According to Rimmer, what was Lister compared with Kochanski?

41 According to Rimmer, why were his eyes watering on his way to the *Nova 5*?

42 How many cameras had Lister blown up trying to explain about their future selves?

43 According to Rimmer, what is there no Eskimo word for?

44 Where was 'Successville'?

45 According to Lister, who was about as popular as 'a horny dog in a Miss Lovely Legs competition'?

46 What did 'Lister' and 'Kochanski' give Kryten as a leaving present?

47 How many floors is it from the cargo decks to the officers' quarters?

48 Who was the Ambassador of the Vindalooian Empire?

49 Who would still be in Corsica peeling spuds if he'd had to share quarters with Lister?

50 How many spare mech heads did the crew take from the *Centauri*?

51 Who's not the 'Robinson Crusoe' type?

52 What was Rimmer the treasurer of?

53 What would be like looking for a needle in a male student's flat?

54 Why hadn't Lister broken the fifth Sacred Law?

55 How much had Lister left in his bank account before joining the Jupiter Mining Corporation?

56 At which rank did Rimmer join the *Enlightenment*?

57 Who always came bottom in geography?

58 Who was forced to run by the mob because they had pictures of him at a transvestite orgy?

59 What would you find under your seat in an Xpress lift?

60 According to Lister, what is being dead like?

61 According to Rimmer, what was the greatest single technological advancement that mankind had ever made?

62 How long had Rimmer been alone with Lister by the time the garbage pod arrived?

63 According to Lister, what had been Rimmer's job in the stores?

64 If the 'high' *Red Dwarf* is succulent and divine, what is the 'low' *Red Dwarf*?

65 What was the best decision that Rimmer ever made?

66 According to Lister, apart from 'Bonehead', what might have Rimmer been called at school?

67 How long does Kryten need to be off-line to discard some old cash files?

68 At which point in the *Complete Works of Shakespeare* would Lister be a dead man?

69 Apart from 'Horace', what did Confidence think Rimmer's 'H' stood for?

70 Where did Lister want the time drive to take them?

71 How did Rimmer keep his underpants?

72 What makes Kryten happy?

73 The day after Rimmer's deathday celebrations, the crew thought that it was Sunday, but what day was it actually?

74 What does Ouroboros mean?

75 What was the name of Rimmer's fictitious sister?

76 Name Captain Voorhese's crocodile/alligator.

77 How did the Ministry of Alteration change people?

78 How long did the King of the Potato people want Lister, Cat and Kryten to stay in quarantine?

79 Who keeps her pants in her sock drawer?

80 Why had Rimmer reported Lister for 'mutiny'?

81 How long was Rimmerworld racked with storms?

82 What did the crew's future selves need from the crew aboard *Starbug*?

83 What is the thing Rimmer is afraid of most in the whole world?

84 From which floor did Lee Harvey Oswald originally plan to shoot President Kennedy?

85 What did Rimmer keep all his valuables in?

86 Who was Mr Beautiful?

87 What is the third-largest city in Vietnam?

88 What were the unreality pockets designed to protect?

89 Which locker was booby-trapped?

90 Where did Rimmer go when he moved out of 'Slob City'?

91 Who was the bass player in Smeg and the Heads?

92 How old was Rimmer when he was kept back a year?

93 What had made Kochanski's Lister sensitive and caring?

94 What would have happened if the gauntlet hadn't aged the manacles?

95 Which bunk was the biggest in the sleeping quarters?

96 What does a 'roll-off deodorant' do?

97 Who's face did the blood-sucking leech have?

98 What does NORWEB stand for?

99 Who did Kryten describe as 'she who must be drooled over'?

100 Why had Lister bought Buck Palace?

The Questions

101 Who was a superlative mathematician?
102 Who got a posting to Titan?
103 What did Rimmer think they should do with Confidence and Paranoia?
104 According to Rimmer, how many cigarettes did he owe Lister?
105 In which prison should President Kennedy have served his sentence?

Word search 7
Bedford Falls

The words listed opposite are 'hidden' in the grid. They may be found written vertically, horizontally or diagonally, and even backwards.

```
I T E N D O L L A R S I V A D S R M M N
M T R I X I E L A B O U C H E S A R R Y
G A S S T A T I O N M Y O L Y H J S S P
J Y K A D R U G S T O R E C E A S H H Y
A E C R W D E R T X A A A B L M B I U K
I L U P K O R A Z C T M S E I I O C B Q
L I D A C C N N E O O N I D A K A K B D
H A J C R M I D V R A O Y F B E R E L N
O B I K E A E M E N H O N O E B D T E O
U A M N W C J A S R K H A R G A I T I P
S M M A O K V W A E F L G D R B N O N S
E U Y R G E I I M G Y U I F O U G Y W R
G I S F N N K L T A E C L A E T H S O E
A R T U A Z S S S N L R L L G T O H R T
N O E V M I N O I A X M U L I F U O B T
A P W H D E A N R M E P M S N F S P X O
H M A E L A H A H K B E R T T H E C O P
P E R N O N C I C N Z S M I J A Y V B G
R S T R N Z O P R A B S I N I T R A M P
O J B Y E L K C U B P O P O H S T E P R
```

104

BANK MANAGER
BEDFORD FALLS
BERT THE COP
BEXLEY
BOARDING HOUSE
BOX BROWNIE
CHRISTMAS EVE
DOC MACKENZIE
DRUGSTORE
DUCKS
EMPORIUM
ERNIE
FRANK CAPRA
GAS STATION
GEORGE BAILEY
GRANDMA WILSON
HENRY
HORACE
ITS A WONDERFUL
  LIFE
JAILHOUSE
JIM
JIMMY STEWART

KOCHANSKI
MA BAILEY
MARTINIS BAR
MARY
MR CULHOON
MR MULLIGAN
MRS DAVIS
MRS HICKETT
MRS HUBBLE
OLD MAN GOWER
ORPHANAGE
PET SHOP
PIANO
POP BUCKLEY
POTTERS POND
SHAMI KEBAB
SYCAMORE
  AVENUE
TEN DOLLARS
TOY SHOP
TRIXIE LABOUCHE
TUBA

'Have you ever actually read any of it?'
Lister, 'Marooned'

This section is entirely based on the four *Red Dwarf* novels. Where the answer can also be found in an episode this will be taken into account.

1 How many years in Cyberhell had Lister been sentenced to?
2 What did the Cat suggest should be worn for killing agonoids?
3 How many grandchildren did Lister have?
4 According to the Cat, in the awards for all-time stupid questions, which one takes the Nobel prize?
5 How big was the domed interior of the Grand Hall?
6 According to Lister, who would have made two more incompetent and useless assistants than Kryten and the Cat?
7 Which 'door' had Lister ignored?
8 According to Rimmer, what did being 'kept down' mean?
9 What's the best way to get into Silicon Heaven?
10 What could a rubber band be in the right hands?
11 What country became the dumping-ground for motor cars?
12 Who took the first watch on the night shift?
13 Who 'Errol Flynned' to the crew's rescue?
14 How did Jimmy and Rimmer escape from prison?

15 How long did Kryten reckon it would take them to reach their own universe?

16 Where had Michael Longman tested his viruses?

17 How much was Lister's mortgage in Bedford Falls?

18 What did Lister's jasmine spell out?

19 Where had Lister first picked up a trail of blood that had led to Kochanski?

20 Who was Rodenbury?

21 What were the 'dove' bullets made of?

22 How many years had Mr Capote been sentenced to?

23 Who snores like a large parrot being strangled in a bucket of soapy water?

24 What had Rimmer suggested they use as a tow-hook to tow the Earth back into the solar system?

25 How many children did the eclair-regurgitating woman have?

26 How soon would it be possible for *Starbug* to drive through the thinning lava?

27 When Lister was fifteen, according to Rimmer, what was Lister's emotional age?

28 How many extra jerks had Rimmer's double done while Rimmer was resting?

29 What were painted on Tonto's revolver?

30 Why does Kryten love anyone who bucked the system?

31 Who was Dr Sabinsky's bodyguard?

32 Who was one circuit short of a Grand Prix track?

33 Why was Mrs Hubble arrested?

34 What colour are meadow saffron flowers?

35 Who was the *Nova 5*'s star demolition engineer?

36 How many guests were there at Rimmer and Helen's wedding?

37 What was seven-year-old Rimmer's rank in class?

38 What had forced Lister to grow up?

39 Who rode a blood-red mare?

40 At what time was Lister supposed to meet the rest of the crew at Niagara Falls?

41 Why had Jimmy gotten life imprisonment?

42 How many years of his sentence must Lister serve before he is permitted visitors?

43 What were 'Lister's' crimes against the Gelf State?

44 Where had Kryten got Rimmer's 'solidogram' body from?

45 How many speakers does Lister's portable wax-blaster have?

46 What garbage was allocated to the Arctic Circle?

47 What direction did Lister and the Cat head in when searching for *Starbug*'s engines?

48 What did paragraph 3(a) of section D27 of the Space Corps manual state? And what did Rimmer read it as?

49 What had Rimmer mistaken Helen's underpants for?

50 According to Rimmer, why doesn't Kochanski like him?

51 How much oxygen did Lister have left when he set out for *Wildfire One*?

52 How many times did Lister hit the alarm clock with the meat tenderizer?

53 How big was Rimmer's fortune?

54 How fast was the Rage moving?

55 How many people were suing Rimmer's mind?

56 Whose eyes were the 'deep blue of a holiday-brochure sky'?

57 How did Rimmer try to alter his school figures?

58 What colour was the letter clipped to the flowers on the 'welcome' pack?

59 What was in 'Lister's' box?

60 How had Lister smuggled Frankenstein aboard *Red Dwarf*?

61 Where did Porky Roebuck throw Rimmer's Space Scout shoes?

62 How was the Rage created?

63 What class was Rimmer in when he was seven?

64 How long did a Bliss high last?

65 Who was 'happier than a bunch of hippies at a ganja harvest'?

66 What was exhibit Q?

67 How long had the crew spent in Better Than Life?

68 How much is four millilitres of sperm?

69 Who was Bedford Falls' down-and-out?

70 Who was a connoisseur of electronic crap?

71 What colour is the finishing tape?

72 How many meetings had Dr Alice Kellerman had with 'Lister'?

73 How old was Dennis McBean?

74 Who snores like a wounded wild hog with asthma?

75 According to Kryten's long-term memory, what did a code 0089/2 signify?

76 Who actually committed the crime that Lister had been charged with in the Backwards universe?

77 What was the reward for information leading to the arrest of Jessie James and his gang?

78 For how long had Lister had his five rasta plaits?

79 What was the name of Admiral Peter Tranter's valet?

80 Why did all holograms bear a two-inch, metallic-looking 'H' on their foreheads?

81 What was Lister's central heating system on Garbage World made from?

82 How much had Rimmer paid for his Louis XIV grand piano?

83 How long did it take Rimmer, Kryten and Cat to hike from *Starbug* to Niagara Falls?

84 Where had Lister and the Cat found one of the landing jets?

85 What did Lister request to be worn at his funeral?

86 Who snores like an asthmatic warthog?

87 What was the Rimmer family motto?

88 What did the first virus that Kryten managed to identify do?

89 Who was the third president of the World Council?

90 Where did Lister usually keep his spare pair of trainers?

91 Who graduated with honours as Flight Co-ordinator first class from the European Space Academy?

92 What year was *Better Than Life* first published?

93 Who had written the crew's confidential reports in their personal files?

94 How wide was Lister's ship-issue snow trowel?

95 What colour is the carpet in the Copacabana Hawaiian Cocktail Bar?

96 What was the name of Henry's wife?

97 Which floor was Rimmer's luxury penthouse suite situated on?

98 Who had 'computer-blue' eyes?

99 How much did Lister get paid at the dentist's?

100 How many parts were there in *Better Than Life*?

101 Name them.

102 Why didn't the astro-stripper harness fit Rimmer properly?

103 What happens to Rimmer's batteries in the Reverse universe?

104 What had happened to the donors on the Reco Programme?

105 Who had done most of the important groundwork for time-freezing and stasis theory?

106 Who runs the boarding-house in Bedford Falls?

107 What were the protesters outside the Forum of Justice protesting about?

108 What had Lister worn for the Summer Party?

109 What rank was Arden Reinhardt?

110 For how long had Kryten washed dishes before realizing he'd been duped?

111 What did Mr Wilmot do for a living?

112 What was the punishment for Cats caught slinking in public?

113 How did Rimmer store the oblivion virus in his light bee?

114 What time did the crew arrange to meet when looking for *Starbug*'s engines?

115 Who had the drive and ambition of a sleeping hippie?

Crossword 6
'Marooned'

The Questions

Across

2 Rimmer thought that Lister had burnt it (6)
4 Where the 'black hole' appeared (12)
7 Grit? (5,5)
9 Lister lost it on a golf course (9)
12 Dogs lick their testicles to take away the taste of this (3,4)
13 How many 'black holes' Holly spotted (4)
15 Book that Lister kept a page from (6)
16 The brothers who made Rimmer Armée du Nord (6)

Down

1 Rimmer's trunk was made of this (7,4)
3 Where the crew were marooned (3,6)
5 Nationality of Rimmer's trunk (8)
6 Kryten wore pink ones (8)
8 Rimmer claimed to have lost his virginity to her (6)
10 The age at which Lister 'nearly dropped his skateboard' (6)
11 You smear it on your mouth ulcer (7)
14 Fuel for heating? (5)

'He's making it up, isn't he?
The bloody book doesn't exist'
Rimmer, 'Quarantine'

State which character said the following, and in which *Red
Dwarf* novel.

1 'We can go anywhen.'
2 'We're getting out of here. We're going back to reality.'
3 'Don't you think that it might be a neatish idea to
   formulate some kind of planny sort of thing first?'
4 'Spanish architecture – not Spanish architecture. It
   reminds me of my first wife. No. God, *nooooo* . . .'
5 'I'm just going to pop down to Old Man Gower's.
   D'you want anything?'
6 'Aren't I a naughty boy? How can you ever forgive
   me?'
7 'They're like mynah birds – they copy things without
   really understanding what it is they're copying.'
8 'Oh smeggy pudding, we've lost our special skills.'
9 'Oh, nice story. Walt Disney could have used a story
   like that.'
10 'I never let Frank touch me. I only want you, my
   purple, jealous darling.'
11 'Believe me, I'd love to join this little expedition, only I
   suffer from a terrible mental affliction known as
   "sanity".'
12 'How the smegging smeg would a toaster know how to
   get out of a black hole?'

13 'Face it, buds, we're deader than dungarees with patterned triangles sewn down the sides to make 'em look like flares.'

14 'Why me? Why is it always me? How many times did I tell you to leave it alone?'

15 'He won't make love to me any more.'

16 'We're not looking for Trouble. But if Trouble comes, it's going to regret the day Mr and Mrs Trouble decided to have it off.'

17 'If you'd just like to slip out of that one, we'll see how it feels.'

18 'Is it me, or is that plastic peckerhead suffering from droid rot?'

19 'We are going to go on a nice little walk down to the cargo bay and then, depending on how we're feeling, who knows, we might even do a spot of abandoning shipping.'

20 'You're winding me up, aren't you? Either that or you've crosswired your vocal chords with your effluence evacuation pipe.'

21 'What do you recommend? A final touristy stroll round, followed by a cream tea?'

22 'Ten dollars! Business is good, Mr Bailey.'

23 'Shut your sissy bitchin', you worthless son of a filthy whore.'

24 'I'm a moron. I'm a nobody. I'm not fit to be alive.'

25 'As God-forsaken hell-holes go, this is definitely one of my favourites.'

26 'I can't eat any more of this dung-beetle filth, boys.'

27 'Earth, no points. *La Terre, zero points.*'

28 'No need to be such a fuss-budget, old love. Improvise.'

29 'Buddy, I didn't just have sex. I had *seeeeeeeeeeeeeeeeex*.'
30 'I'd give it another twenty-five glimbarts.'
31 'Oh, lemme see. There was some Aprapaho, some Navajo, some Idunno . . .'
32 'How about I cover the ceiling with your brains?'
33 'I take it all back. He's still the giant intellect he always was.'
34 'God speed.'
35 'Where's Yvette? I've been waiting for ages. I need those course calculations.'
36 'Can I do you any small personal favours in return for extravagant gifts of real estate and suchlike?'
37 'Puncture the space-time continuum, eh? Create the required energy. Okey-dokey, here we gokey.'
38 'We couldn't just waive the rules for once?'
39 'Sorry to keep you waiting, sir. Would you like a pick'n'mix or an off-the-peg?'
40 'Wonderful. I like a meal with a happy ending.'
41 'Oh, I don't think they masturbate excessively, sir. Not for young men of their age.'
42 'I already have a plan: put on the jacket, grab a bazookoid and let those bad-ass robot dudes eat laser.'
43 'Say "hi" to Jesus for me.'
44 'Good luck with the test, Billy-Joe.'

'I've come to regard you as
. . . people . . . I've met'
Rimmer, 'Holoship'

1 What did Lister steal from Adolf Hitler?
2 What did the hillbilly use as a fuel canister for his still?
3 Who did the Cat think Caroline Carmen looked like?
4 Where was George McIntyre's 'welcome back' reception held?
5 Whose dad was 'secretly knocking off' Rimmer's mum?
6 How did Lister describe 'Bent Bob'?
7 Who took over from Old Doc Diagnostics?
8 How much did Jim and Bexley give to Henry?
9 Who did Will Carton make his deputy?
10 On which of Petersen's arms was 'Denmark Forever' tattooed?
11 Where did Spanners work?
12 Why was Bull Heinman so named?
13 Who was Miss Yo-Yo Knickers?
14 Why did Petersen leave Triton?
15 Who did Rimmer call 'a pop-eyed balding git'?
16 Who was Michael R. McGruder's father?
17 Whose boot did Sheriff Kryten trip over?
18 Which cigars did Admiral Tranter smoke?
19 What nationality was Janine Rimmer?
20 Where did Rimmer's mum head for when he lost his race?
21 Why did Selby think Lister had no chance with Kochanski?

22 Why had Lister split up with Lise Yates?

23 How much did Billy Belief give Will Carton to become his deputy?

24 Which type of gun did George McIntyre commit suicide with?

25 When had Carton last had a bath?

26 Where had Yvonne McGruder fainted?

27 What was odd about Will Carton's pocket-watch?

28 According to Lister, where could Michelle Fisher have got a job?

29 Where did Lister hide Caroline Carmen?

30 Who beat her steel truncheon on Lister's locker door?

31 How old was Tommy Tate?

32 What was 'Thicky' Holden's Christian name?

33 Which of Lister's fingers did Famine eat?

34 Who smoked black cigarettes?

35 How did Brett Riverboat stop Jimmy from cursing?

36 Who took over from Will Carton as sheriff?

37 Where did Lorraine suddenly have to move to?

38 What colour were Death's eyes?

39 What had Frank, John and Howard had installed in their long-term memories?

40 List the contents of Duane Dibbley's case.

41 What did Dicky Duckworth mouth to Rimmer when he crossed the finishing line?

42 What were 'Lister's' foster parents called?

43 How long had Denis and Josie been travelling for?

44 How tall was Lieutenant-Colonel Michael R. McGruder?

45 What was the name of Admiral Peter Tranter's secretary?

46 At what time had Lister lost his virginity to Michelle Fisher?

47 How old was Dicky Duckworth?

48 Where was the hotel that Lister/Rimmer had taken Lise Yates?

49 According to Gilbert, who was an 'artist beyond comparison'?

50 Who was Jeff Calculator's wife?

51 Where had Yvonne McGruder disembarked from *Red Dwarf*?

52 What was Lister's pet name for Caroline Carmen?

53 Who did Rimmer think was 'Mary Queen of Scots'?

54 Who had been Michael McGruder's best friend?

55 What had Duncan Potson taught Rimmer to do in Junior A?

56 Who was Rimmer's gym teacher?

57 How long had Rimmer been with the company when he was invited to dine at the Captain's table?

58 What had happened to Lew Pemberton since Lister had last seen him?

59 How long had Denis and Josie known each other?

60 What was Pythagoras's solution to everything?

61 How tall was Trixie LaBouche?

62 Name Billy Doyle's cologne.

63 How many hideously expensive gold stars had Admiral Peter Tranter ordered?

64 Who first showed Lister to his sleeping quarters when he joined *Red Dwarf*?

65 What did Tim do for a living?

66 At what time did the Captain request the pleasure of Mr A. J. Rimmer?

67 Where did Admiral Tranter plan to go with his wife after Ace's departure?

68 Who did Thicky Holden marry?

69 What did Petersen call Project Wildfire?

70 How many soldiers were there in 'Arnie Rimmer's death machine'?

71 According to Lister, who was the anti-Lister?

72 What rank was Sam Murray?

73 How long had Juanita's Oscar 'thank you' speech lasted?

74 What did Petersen do to warrant being in jail on Europa?

75 Who was gay on Kochanski's *Red Dwarf*?

76 What rank was George McIntyre?

77 How old was 'Lister' when he was adopted by the Thorntons?

78 Which one of Lister's sons did Rimmer see die in the drive room?

79 Who did Rimmer refer to as 'Captain Smug Git'?

80 How many beers had Petersen drunk while waiting for Lister to show?

81 What score beat Caldicott's three and two?

82 What had Yvonne McGruder been hit on the head with prior to her date with Rimmer?

83 What planet was Tranter stationed on?

84 What had Rimmer's brothers made a swing out of?

85 How did Captain Hollister describe Rimmer in his report?

86 Whose records got mixed up with Peter Tranter's?

87 What rank was Caroline Carmen?

88 According to Holly, what was the only thing Lister had in common with Petersen?

89 How old was Lindy Lou?

90 Where did Petersen wake after he got ratted in Oslo?

91 What rank was Peter Tranter?

92 Who did Kryten think was beginning to look 'so pasty'?

93 Who was *Red Dwarf*'s female boxing champion?

94 What were Tonto Jitterman's last words?

95 How old was Lister when his dad died?

96 Who was Donald?

97 What did the hermit dress his pig in?

98 What job did Tranter threaten to give Spanners if he had one more outburst?

99 Who did Kryten call a 'silly old trout'?

100 What rank was Elvis Presley?

101 On which day does Bull Heinman humiliate the 'wets, weirdoes and fatties'?

102 What company did Sebastian Doyle work for?

103 Who always wears a white suit and a big floppy hat?

104 Who had a gene pool no bigger than a spider's piss puddle?

105 Which position does Spanners hold in the Space Corps?

106 Whose hobbies include horse riding and ballet?

107 How long did the Apocalypse Boys give Sheriff Kryten to get out of town?

108 What had the hillbilly been using the engine in the grain store for?

109 Where did Rimmer claim to have met Sandra?

110 How much had Petrovitch expected to make by selling a hundred Better Than Life headbands?

111 What was Peter Tranter known to his peers as?

112 What did Thicky Holden think a glacier was?

Word search 8
'Duct Soup'

The words listed opposite are 'hidden' in the grid. They may be found written vertically, horizontally or diagonally, and even backwards.

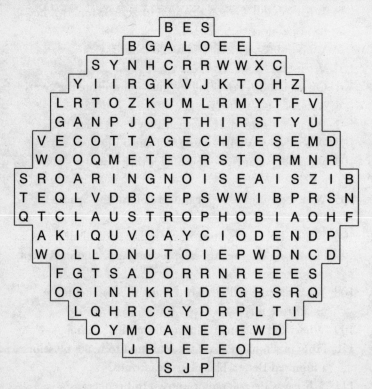

BACKUP GENERATOR
BATH
CLAUSTROPHOBIA
COMIC
COTTAGE CHEESE
CRYING
DEGREES
DUCT
LAUNDRY
METEOR STORM
NINETY TWO
PEACH SLICES
PIPES
ROARING NOISE
SHOWER
SLEEP
SPANNER
SWEATING
THIRSTY
UNDERWEAR
WATER

'Pussycat Willum!'

1 What did the Cat think was wrong with Lister's face?
2 What would the Cat rather wear than agree with 'Goalpost head'?
3 What 'essentials' did the Cat take aboard *Starbug* when *Red Dwarf* was ambushed by the 'black holes'?
4 What did the Cat think looked like Frankenstein's hand-me-downs?
5 How many racks of suits did the Cat want to take into stasis?
6 What did the Cat suggest Lister do with his remaining fifty-eight minutes of life?
7 According to the Cat, what is more important than Lister's life?
8 What did the Cat think was going on in the Nogard dna Egroeg?
9 Where did the Cat suggest they look for their 'lost' four days?
10 According to Rimmer, what should the Cat wear with the cavalry twill trousers to be dignified and fashionable at the same time?
11 In the Cat's Better Than Life wardrobe, if it's three o'clock for his shirts, what time is it for his socks?
12 According to the Cat, how long is five hanika?
13 According to the Cat, who was the Mexican dude who robbed people?

14 How does the Cat do his laundry?

15 On which day did the Cat have 'double nothing' at school?

16 What has always been the Cat's lucky number?

17 What was the Cat's 'ultimate question'?

18 How long did the Cat want to control Lister for?

19 Who did the Cat refer to as 'Stan and Ollie'?

20 What did the Cat say he might have to do if Rimmer took his 'shiny thing' away?

21 What had the Cat salvaged from the 'Red Dwarf' planetoid?

22 What did the Cat say the 'footprints' were the size of?

23 According to Lister, what size are the Cat's feet?

24 According to the Cat, who's had 'more rams than a field of sheep'?

25 What was the Cat's favourite game in Better Than Life?

Jigword
'Tongue-tied'

From the song below, take the words highlighted and fit them into the grid below, crossword-fashion, wherever space allows.

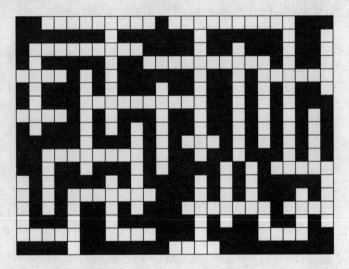

Whoo! **Whenever** you are near me
I get tongue-tied baby, whoo!

When I saw you for the **first** time (first time)
My knees began to **quiver** (quiver)
And I **got** a **funny feeling** (feeling)
In my **kidneys** and my **liver**
(**Digestive** system, baby)

My hands they **started** shaking (shaking)
And my **heart** began a-**thumping**
(Boom–boom–boom)
My **breakfast** left my body
(**Huey**, huey, huey)
Now **darling** tell me **something**

Why do you make me
Tongue-tied (tongue-tied) tongue-tied
Whenever you are **near** me (whenever you are)
I'm tie-tongue (tie-tongue) tie-tongue (tie-tongue)
Whenever you're in **town** (in town)
You **make** me feel a **clown girl**
Yes you make me
Tongue-tongue (tied-tied) tongue-tied
Why can't I tell you **clearly** (why can't I tell you)
Tie-tied, tongue-tongue, (tie-tied) tongue-tied
Whenever you're **around**
(Around, ba-dap-bap-bow-boo-dow)

I **saw** you 'cross the **dancefloor dancing)**
I thought of **birds** and **bees**
(**Reproductive** system, baby)
But when I tried to **speak** to you (talk talk)
My tongue **unravelled** to my **knees**
(**Flibberdy**-flibberdy-flob)
I **tried** to say 'I **love** you' (love you)
But it came out kind of **wrong** girl
(Whoo-who-who-hooo)
It sounded like:
'Nunubididoo' (tongue-tied)
Nuh mr nuhmurh ni nong nurl

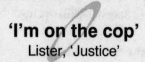

'I'm on the cop'
Lister, 'Justice'

1 Who said that 'Rimmer was a brave man trapped inside the body of a coward'?
2 Who did Rimmer try to chat up at Caligula's orgy?
3 What would be the by-product of Rimmer inventing the Tension Sheet?
4 How old was Cashier Number Four when Lister fell in love with her?
5 Who used to practise kissing on his own hand?
6 What did the coloured triangle on the Blerion's robes signify?
7 Who was Mercedes?
8 According to Rimmer, what is love?
9 What did Peter Tranter's mistress call him?
10 How old was the Cat when he had sex for the first time?
11 What would Lister rather do than kiss Rimmer?
12 In terms of wordage, with whom did Lister have a better relationship than Kochanski?
13 How did Lister die at the age of ninety-eight?
14 Who did the Cat lose his virginity to?
15 Why could Rimmer never get a date?
16 What did Lister give Rimmer as a deathday present?
17 How did Lister practice unhooking bras?
18 Who suffered from gonorrhoea and syphilis so badly they could hardly pee?

19 Who was Cashier Number Four married to?
20 According to Lister, what makes us different from animals?
21 Who did 'Rimmer's mum' describe as a 'wild stallion'?
22 What had Juanita's mother warned her against?
23 Who did Billy-Joe want to ask out on a date?
24 What happens to Lister every time he sees a Parker Knoll?
25 What did Rimmer try to do to the Sphinx on his stag night?
26 Where did Rimmer suggest he and Lister take the two brunettes from supplies?
27 What did Rimmer try to bribe Lister with so that he wouldn't tell anyone else about his single sexual liaison?
28 Who makes a sound like a rusty gate when making love?
29 To whom did Rimmer claim to have lost his virginity?
30 What would the Cat have eaten his mother alive to do?
31 How long did Ace like to spend making love?
32 Where did Lister's confidence go to when he walked up to Kochanski to ask her out?
33 According to Rimmer, why did Lister use the AR machine?
34 How did Rimmer find out that Lister had dated Lise Yates?
35 What did the Cat think of Betty Rubble?
36 What did Lister think Silicon Heaven was?
37 How long had it taken for Juanita's ex-lovers to pass through the witness stand?
38 What did Rimmer say had happened to his date for the Captain's dinner?

39 According to Rimmer, what was Lister's type?

40 According to Lister, why had Rimmer joined the Love Celibacy Society?

41 According to ship's regulations, how many times a day must you have sex on the *Enlightenment*?

42 According to Rimmer, whose parents could have been brother and sister?

43 Where would you find a pair of testicle handcuffs?

44 Where was the all-female naturist beach that Rimmer had a photograph of?

45 Who makes love like a Japanese meal?

46 What would Bongo be covered in at lunchtime?

47 Which cashier did Lister fall in love with?

48 Whose short skirts made Rimmer 'really horny'?

49 When was Natalina Pushkin free for sex?

50 When did Rimmer and Lister snog?

51 How old was Rimmer when he 'got off' with Fiona Barrington?

52 What was Rimmer trying to clone on Rimmerworld?

53 How long was the guarantee on the AR machine's groinal attachment?

54 How many children had 'Lister' fathered?

55 Who's had less sex than a lettuce?

56 Who had an artificial nose?

57 Who would Rimmer have happily killed if he was 'on the job'?

**'There's a wise old cat saying
which I think applies in this situation'**
Cat, 'Stasis Leak'

State the characters in *Red Dwarf* who said the following, and in which episode.

1 'That's a long time, Dave, for a man of your drives.'
2 'I'll put the rubber room on stand-by, sir.'
3 'There's no percentage in being a boy racer, Kryten.'
4 'It's possible to make diamonds out of pencils?'
5 'Remember this, you're getting my underwear bill, buddy.'
6 'Of course not, use your loaf.'
7 'As a mark of respect, we thought on Sunday at 12 o'clock we could have a minute's flatulence.'
8 'Ah, Miss McGruder, where were we?'
9 'OK, homeboys, let's posse.'
10 'Hey, I hear they do good bread and water here, buddy.'
11 'I've just been molested by Tutankhamun's horny grandma. Of course I'm not smegging all right.'
12 'Come, soul sibling, let us prepare some refreshments.'
13 'Oh, that's better. Kill two birds with one shower.'
14 'Oh, who woke *him* up?'
15 'Everything tickety-boo?'
16 'It's been a hundred per cent success, sir. In fact, it's been a five hundred per cent success.'
17 'Last time it was hors-d'oeuvres, this time it's lunch.'

18 '*Absolument*, Mr Rimmer, I'll be along lickety-split.'

19 'OK, which one of you chimpanzees did this?'

20 'It's chick city, bud. Five sisters and they're all hotter than a Mustang's exhaust.'

21 'I'm no stranger to the land of scoff.'

22 'Lister, have you ever been hit over the head with a welding mallet?'

23 'Now come on, get your kit off and I'll go and slip into my Batman outfit.'

24 'I don't think he meant to do that. It probably just plopped out.'

25 'Well that's put a crimp on an otherwise damn fine plan.'

26 'Not here, it's too sandy.'

27 'A big, fat woman with thighs the size of a hippo's.'

28 'These strides are too tackle-tight, Officer BB. I can barely cruise.'

29 'Lister, have you been at that marijuana gin again?'

30 'Lister to *Red Dwarf*. We have in our midst a complete smegpot.'

31 'He who lives by the rule book, dies by the rule book.'

32 'I didn't know robots got PMT.'

33 'Move so much as an eyebrow, boys, and you're dog meat.'

34 'All I said was "open the next one".'

35 'Look at him – with the right boots, he could be marching into Poland.'

36 'The menu looks interesting. I think I'll try the chicken.'

37 'Don't give me the Star Trek crap, it's too early in the morning.'

38 'I'm getting a mite panicky here.'

39 'I don't know. I don't speak alien, you gimboid.'

40 'Thanksi veryski muchski, budski.'

41 'I'll take that as a No, then.'

42 'Anybody got any opera glasses?'

43 'Healthy – who cares? Pork away!'

44 'I feel like I'm having a baby.'

45 'Kryten, get the hacksaw and follow me.'

46 'Do you know I had you marked down as a bit of a madman?'

47 'It's not the place, Lister, it's the company.'

48 'Wow, we won't see the like of those sort of days again.'

49 'My God, a G-string!'

50 'I suggest we ambulate as fast as the local gravity will allow.'

51 'First meal I ever had where the container tastes better than the food!'

52 'Smoke me a kipper, I'll be back for breakfast.'

53 'I thought I could navigate at light speed but I just can't wrap my head round it.'

54 'What do you think of the picket fence?'

55 'Oh my God, it's the missus!'

56 'You know what I'd really like, I'd really like to make love to a guy like you.'

57 'You're hallucinating. Put the gun down.'

58 'Why should I do that? I've never heard of her.'

59 'That's OK, I'm sure there'll be another chance for you to cock it up again.'

60 'That information is security protected.'

61 'But that must mean the rest of the crew are better than you, then.'

62 'Yeah, they could take a Pot Noodle and turn it into food.'

63 'I propose we hit it hard and hit it fast with a major, and I mean major, leaflet campaign.'

64 'Well, I wouldn't like to be stuck behind one in a cinema.'

65 'Lie mode. Of course it will work, sir. No worries.'

66 'How was I supposed to know a chicken vindaloo was going to cause all this?'

67 'That's a classic, that is. That's a classic.'

68 'Excuse me, could I possibly distract you for just a brief second?'

69 'Right, let's send them back to their ship and get the hell out of here before they get their smeg together.'

70 'I'm sorry sir, I didn't mean to steal your thunder.'

71 'I don't want you to panic, Arnold. I want you to stay absolutely calm. I'm coming out in a moment and I want you to keep your cool.'

72 'I tell you, if I was dead you most certainly could not swing me around in here.'

73 'Man, I could smell you if you was on Mars!'

74 'I'm not fat, I'm hunky.'

75 'I don't believe we've had the pleasure of meeting your handsome young friends.'

76 'We're not looking for a fight, but if he thinks he can mix it with the *Red Dwarf* posse on their homeboy turf, the sucker's leaving as scrap metal.'

77 'You want me to follow your cords?'

78 'No part of me would ever be seen alive in sandals.'

79 'Perhaps a Banana Bomb, sir?'

80 'It's a piece of crypto-fascist bourgeois crap.'

81 'I've been tongue-hockeyed to death.'

82 'He's such a child, that boy.'

83 'Well, trash my shorts! What a funny-looking dog!'

84 'Er, Holly, where's my arm?'

85 'I'm too mature for this. I'm just going to sit here and read my comic.'

86 'Right. Let's get out of here. I badly need to floss a piece of roasted dead person out of my teeth!'

87 'Yawn-a-rama city, we know an admiral.'

88 'Totally tubular!'

89 'Strike a light, I'm a genius again.'

90 'Holly, that's an order, you stupid, ugly goit.'

91 'What was it, a cheap razor? It's just not worth buying them from garages, is it?'

92 'Whatever that was, let's hope it's had lunch.'

93 'Even it out, take out the flaky bits.'

94 'Can I help it if I happen to be sexy?'

Word search 9
Characters

The words listed opposite are 'hidden' in the grid. They may be found written vertically, horizontally or diagonally, and even backwards.

ACE	INQUISITOR
ARLENE	J F KENNEDY
BEXLEY	JAKE BULLET
BILLY DOYLE	JIM
BINKS	KOCHANSKI
CAMILLE	KRYTEN
CAT	LEGION
CAT PRIEST	LISE YATES
CHEN	LISTER
CONFIDENCE	MARILYN MONROE
DEB	MELLY
DOG	NIRVANAH CRANE
DR LANSTROM	PARANOIA
DUANE DIBBLEY	PETERSEN
EINSTEIN	PYTHAGORAS
ELVIS PRESLEY	QUEEG
FRANKENSTEIN	RATHBONE
GILBERT	RIMMER
GORDON	SELBY
HECTOR	STAN LAUREL
HITLER	TALKIE TOASTER
HOLLISTER	THE TAXMAN
HOLLY	THICKY HOLDEN
HUDZEN	TODHUNTER

'What are you looking for?'
Genny mutant, 'Polymorph'

1 What shape was the 'Friday the 13th' video?
2 On which level was Lister placed into stasis?
3 On which arm was the Gestapo officer's swastika armband?
4 On which wrist did Paranoia wear his watch?
5 With which hand did Kryten peel potatoes?
6 How many full 360-degree turns does it take to remove Kryten's head?
7 From which hand and which eye did Kryten build his 'tarantula'?
8 What packaging did the TIV game come in?
9 Which twin had the blue dummy in his mouth?
10 What was tied to the steering-column in *Blue Midget*?
11 Which boot is Lister polishing at the table on *Starbug*?
12 What did Duane Dibbley use as a mirror?
13 What make was Rimmer's alarm clock?
14 Which season was featured on Lister's London Jets poster?
15 How many soldiers were there in the German firing squad?
16 What was Lister eating during the routine maintenance of dispenser one-seven-two?
17 What is drawn on the Cat's plaster cast?
18 What was Lister reading on the journey to the *Nova 5*?
19 Where does the skutter first put the thermometer when taking Lister's temperature?

20 Who was Android 72264Y?

21 How many balls and cues were there on the grav-pool table?

22 How was the fishing note signed?

23 Into which ear does Kryten plug his download cable?

24 How many flashbacks did it take for Rimmer to realize that he had told Lister about his brief sex life?

25 How many times did Lister hit his sock with a hammer?

26 What kind of waistcoat did the exam chef wear?

27 What artificial intelligence system does Talkie Toaster have?

28 What did Kryten throw into Rimmer's bunk?

29 Which nostril did Lister pluck with the cooking tongs?

30 What did 'Rimmer' use to cut off 'Lister's' dreadlocks?

31 When is Rimmer's 'H' present but *not* in his forehead?

32 From which deck on *Starbug* did 'Ace' take off?

33 What shape were Professor Mamet's earrings?

34 Which hand does the Inquisitor wear his gauntlet on?

35 Which way did the release wheel on the fire extinguisher turn?

36 Which pocket did Rimmer (Ace) take his party tooter from?

37 How old was Anne Gill?

38 What shape were young Lister's shades?

39 Which planet is featured on a badge on the sleeve of Lister's spacesuit?

40 In which episode does a skutter fire a gun?

41 What did Lister carry Kryten's Spare Head Two in?

42 When did Lister drink out of a blue lager can?

43 What did Rimmer's brothers keep the ants in?

44 How many cigarettes did Lister have in his hat when he told Rimmer of his dad's death?

45 What rank was Tracey Johns?

46 What was the airline at Idlewild Airport?

47 What visual system does Talkie Toaster have?

48 What was the picture on Lister's jigsaw?

49 Where would you find an oversized pink dummy?

50 Where does Kochanski first put Frankenstein?

51 Which hand did Rimmer 'print' in his engineering exam?

52 Which side is the steering wheel in Sebastian Doyle's limo?

53 What was the registration of the T72?

54 Where would you find a spotty oven glove?

55 Which fruit is Kochanski eating straight out of a tin?

56 What was written on Lise's 'gravestone'?

57 What did the poster on the Rimmer's quarters door say?

58 How many watts did the sign in the Hologram Suite state?

59 Where was Chen's tattoo?

60 What did Rimmer see instead of the cougar?

61 What was the Cat's belt motif on his gold spacesuit?

62 How many babies did the skutters have?

63 Where was the Stars and Stripes flag situated on President Kennedy's car?

64 Which leg did Lister tie his scarf around?

65 What did the Cat wear to enter Better Than Life?

66 How many times does Kryten defibrillate Lister?

67 How many points were there on Sheriff Kryten's badge?

68 Which way does the embryo refrigeration unit door open?

The Questions

69 Whose teddy wears an army helmet?

70 What is written on the exit doors of the Rimmer Experience?

71 When did the sleeping quarters have pine furniture?

72 On which level did the Cat lose his tooth?

73 How many people were travelling in J.F.K.'s car?

74 Who was carrying the wicker fishing box?

75 Into which of Lister's temples does Kryten inject the mind enema?

76 Where was number plate No. 2G22394 issued?

77 What was odd about the Cat Priest's hands?

78 Which cuff does the Cat take an extra playing card out of?

79 How many potatoes does the Cat juggle?

80 How did the Cat try to catch Lennon and McCartney?

81 What letters were left on Lister's Scrabble holder?

82 Who was the brunette on the *Nova 5*?

83 What did the DNA modifier turn Lister into first?

84 In which leg did Lister shoot Kochanski with the crossbow?

85 How many speed bumps did the crew go over during their group hallucination?

86 What number was on the simulant's bazookoid?

87 What make was the cine camera used to film J.F.K.?

88 How did Miss Lola take the cork out of the gulping whisky bottle?

89 Which of her arms did Kochanski 'cut off'?

90 How many eyes do the skutters have?

91 What was chalked on the back of Rimmer's school blazer?

92 When did the Cat wear roller skates?

93 Which way does Lister's shower door open?

94 What's on Thomas Allman's bedside cabinet?

95 What did Lister use as candlesticks?

96 Which of the *Nova 5*'s girls had blonde hair?

97 Where did Lister place Kryten's guilt chip after removing it?

98 What was written on the note pinned to Kryten's suit?

99 What was embroidered on the Cat's bib?

100 What condition follows 'mauve'?

101 When did the Cat wear curlers?

102 On which cheek did Holly have a 'computer rash'?

103 What was written on the namecard that Rimmer was holding up for Lister in the landing bay?

104 What was the registration of Sebastian Doyle's limo?

105 Which instrument does the 'high' Kryten play?

106 Which fingernail did Lister put in the pencil sharpener?

107 Who had a tattoo on the back of her right hand?

108 Which shoulder did Kryten throw his groinal attachment hose over?

109 How many members of staff met Lister as he drew up outside his English mansion?

110 How many candles were there on Rimmer's deathday cake?

111 How many wheels were there on Lister's space bike?

112 What were Confidence and Paranoia eating in the drive room?

113 How many pieces does Kryten cut off Lister's arm?

114 How many showers were there in the stasis leak shower?

115 What was the date when Lister was placed under the grav-pool table?

116 How tall was Jane Air?
117 How many hanging medals did Rimmer have on his dress uniform?
118 How many rows of pearls does Rimmer's mum wear?
119 What time were the crew playing cards in the Texas Book Depository?

Word grid 1

Unscramble the names of songs featured in *Red Dwarf*, then place them horizontally in the grid. If you have placed them in the correct order the vertical column marked with an arrow will spell out the name of another *Red Dwarf* song.

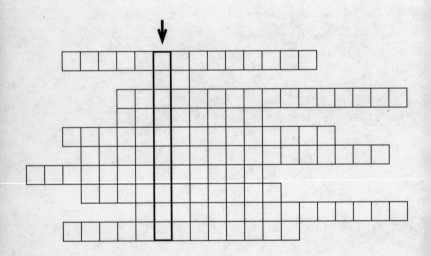

The Questions

NDIGOSLGNIN
MO
SUEFYISOFLOHEMT
PYADEYTAPDHAH
EATAGMDTAIDNEYNN
DYTOEOVEOGLOB
TELMEONTYHMFOO
FDAHFLUSRDFERWE
OGNHOIHN
EDONDEADYALEKYDNO

'Officer Bud Babe!'

1 Where was Kochanski brought up?
2 Who had Kochanski's former boyfriend left her for?
3 Why doesn't Kryten like Kochanski?
4 According to Kochanski, what is the fourth favourite pastime aboard *Starbug*?
5 What did Kochanski do the first time she saw *Gone with the Wind*?
6 What had Kochanski tried to learn in order to fit in on *Starbug*?
7 What does the Cat call Kochanski?
8 Which suit was the ace that Kochanski picked out second?
9 For how long did Lister want to turn Rimmer off in order to go on a date with Kochanski's hologram?
10 What was Kochanski's pony called?
11 At what age did Kochanski have flying lessons?
12 Whose leg wax did Kochanski find under the medi-scanner?
13 How long had Lister spent on Backwards without Kochanski?
14 Which game did Kochanski choose?
15 Why did Confidence say Kochanski would be interested in Lister?
16 According to Kryten, what does Kochanski's bedside manner lack?

17 For how long had 'Kochanski' been packing the Cat's bags?

18 How did Lister first save Kochanski from non-space?

19 According to the Cat, what is Kochanski's most nauseating feature?

20 How many years did Kochanski spend at cyber-school?

21 How old was Kochanski when she spent all her time in Pride and Prejudice World?

22 Who had been Kochanski's lover in the alternative reality?

Crossword 7
'The End'

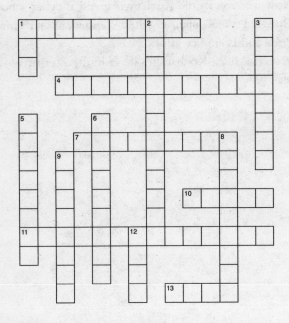

The Questions

Across

1 Lethal radiation (7,3)
4 The Holy Cat Mother (12)
7 Ship's captain (9)
10 It's coming home! (5)
11 Lister's stasis sentence (8,6)
13 Lister's mate (4)

Down

1 Felis sapiens (3)
2 How many years Lister was in stasis (5,7)
3 Welsh hologram (8)
5 Lister's drinking partner (8)
6 One of *Red Dwarf*'s officers (9)
8 What killed the crew (9)
9 Rimmer's status (8)
12 One of what Rimmer keeps failing (4)

Word search 10
Kochanski

The words listed opposite are 'hidden' in the grid. They may be found written vertically, horizontally or diagonally, and even backwards.

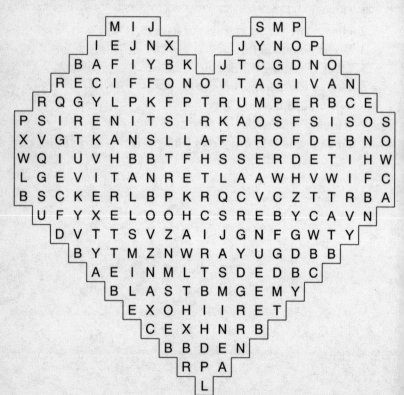

ALTERNATIVE
BEDFORD FALLS
BETTER THAN LIFE
BEXLEY
BUD BABE
COTTAGE CHEESE
CYBER SCHOOL
FIJI
JASMINE
JIM
KRISTINE
LISTER
NAVIGATION OFFICER
PINBALL SMILE
PONY
PSIREN
RED DWARF
SYCAMORE AVENUE
TRUMPER
TWINS
WHITE DRESS

'Have infection, will travel'
Male simulant, 'Gunmen of the Apocalypse'

1 Where was the first human born?
2 Which hospital drama had Lister seen every episode of?
3 What did Kryten think the Heimlich manoeuvre would cure?
4 Why had Kochanski been brought out of deep sleep early?
5 How did Kryten first suggest that Lister deal with the Epideme virus?
6 What's the hologrammatic equivalent of 'foaming dog fever'?
7 Who was the doctor in Bedford Falls?
8 How did Kryten insert the nanobots into Lister?
9 Where does Lister have two little moles?
10 For how long had 'Ace' quarantined 'Arnie'?
11 How many teeth does the Cat have?
12 What time was it when Lister woke up Rimmer when he had mutated pneumonia?
13 What percentage of Blerion males were impotent?
14 When did Lister crack his spine in three places?
15 How many teeth does Lister have?
16 At what age did Rimmer's self-respect die?
17 What had Kryten made Lister's dental cap from?
18 Who had world-class bad breath?
19 What was sad about Lister's uncle?

20 How long does it take the Epideme virus to kill its victim?

21 How did John Ewe die?

22 What did Rimmer claim he was allergic to?

23 What did Rimmer do to Lister so that he nearly needed brain surgery?

24 What does the Epideme virus do?

25 After drowning, how much water did Lister have in his lungs?

26 How had Rimmer contracted the holovirus?

27 What job had Lister found in his Cyberhell?

28 Which disk had Kryten mistaken for his hypnotherapy disk?

29 Which of Kryten's legs was cut off with a holowhip?

30 Who died of acute bullet poisoning?

31 Which optical effects don't humans possess?

32 How long had Caroline Carmen been dead?

33 According to Lister, if you go through life never experiencing pain then you are no better than what?

34 Who told Jim that Carol was dying?

35 How long did it take Kryten to return Rimmer's DNA back to normal?

36 What ailments did Lister wake up with in Cyberhell?

37 What was the only way to save Lister from the Epideme virus?

38 How much did the Cat bet Lister that Kryten was dead?

39 What had the crew of the SS *Augustus* died from?

40 Who had needed a friendly hand to hold, up until the age of twenty-five, when he underwent dental surgery?

41 What indicated that the luck virus had worn off Lister?

42 On which day was Lister 'joyfully brought to life'?

43 If Henry LeClerk had succeeded in poisoning the mineral spring, who would have been wiped out in three weeks?

44 According to Kochanski, when men get the common cold, what do they think they have?

45 What does Cyberfoam do?

46 How long did Rimmer threaten to quarantine Lister for?

47 What did Kochanski use to dress Kryten's leg wound?

48 Who killed Dr Richard Kimble's wife?

49 What did Lister think would be nicer than smoking Spanish tobacco and drinking Spanish coffee?

50 For how long had Lister had space mumps?

51 Whose 'wanger' did Petersen 'whack with the staple gun'?

52 Who did Lister see face the firing squad?

53 How much time had Lister gained by losing his arm?

54 What had Billy-Joe grabbed during his bar fight with the Commander?

55 According to Kochanski, what was Lister allergic to?

56 What was Kryten's serenity reading as he was escorted to the Department of Justice?

57 What's not uncommon after a prolonged period in deep sleep?

58 After Lister's encounter with Famine, which three parts of his anatomy didn't hurt?

59 Who videoed Rimmer's death?

60 What was Lister's third least favourite way of bidding the long 'so long'?

61 Why was the Epideme virus created?

62 How old did 'Lister' look when Rimmer saw him die in the future echo?

63 How did Kryten think the oriental male could have died?

64 How did Kryten cut off Lister's arm?

65 At what speed had the oxygen tank been travelling when it hit Kryten in the solar plexus?

66 Who did Lister say had killed 'Rimmer'?

67 How had Confidence killed Paranoia?

68 What happened to Lister while he was being interrogated at the police station in the Backwards universe?

69 What mood stabilizer did Kryten suggest the crew take?

70 What was the taxman instructed to do by the Revenue if Rimmer couldn't pay his tax demand?

71 Who suffered from silicon rickets?

72 Where did General Patton have his sinuses drained?

73 What did Kryten attach Lister's artificial arm to to make it function?

74 What did War's tomahawk do to Lister?

75 How did Lister's grandmother die?

76 What had Kochanski injected into Caroline Carmen's arm?

77 How did Rimmer describe his own remains?

78 What did Lister temporarily repair his dental cap with?

79 What was in the fourth vial that Kochanski picked while under the influence of the Luck virus?

80 What was Kryten's Spare Head Three 'half raddled' with?

81 Which part of his body did Lister lose in the acid rain?

82 Why couldn't Rimmer let Lister, Cat and Kryten out of quarantine?

83 How long did the live broadcast of a rectal examination last?

84 What's one of Rimmer's worst nightmares?

85 What did Lister think his peritonitis was?

86 How much of the Epideme virus had been left in Lister after cutting off his arm?

87 At what age should Rimmer have had his Encyclo chip implanted?

88 Who is claustrophobic?

89 Which of Lister's teeth had Kryten removed?

90 Why did the Cat want the keys to the medical cabinet?

91 What were the medical facilities aboard *Starbug*?

92 Where was the release catch concealed on Rimmer's body?

93 Which side of Lister's brain controls the right side of his body?

94 How much had Juanita's personality surgery cost her?

'Why did I always turn to page 47 and start drawing little beards and moustaches on the sperms?'

Lister, 'White Hole'

State which character said the following, and in which *Red Dwarf* novel.

1 'OK, people. Wagons roll!'
2 'Four a.m. Time for you to catch some zeds, old chum-burger.'
3 'Another one I owe you, you old lemon tartlet.'
4 'There's more fiddling goes on up there than in the court of Old King Cole.'
5 '*Avez-vous* some, uh, Alka-Seltzer?'
6 'Hang on. Hang about. I'm not all here, mate.'
7 'No thanks, acne face.'
8 'Are you kidding? I wouldn't use this to buff my shoes.'
9 'Mr Lister, I presume.'
10 'Don't look at me, buddy. You're the one who promised to make this handsome dude French-kiss your butt-hole.'
11 'Bewdiful.'
12 'Yoo-hoo! I'm your worst nightmare, please let me in.'
13 'No, I don't want to, I want you, Deki. Just you. No . . .'
14 'You feel possibly, perhaps, you're maybe man enough to probably stop me, you reckon?'

15 'Metaphor, shmetaphor. They bleed, don't they?'

16 'Will you two reckless nincompoops for God's sake stop smegging about!'

17 'Nobody crosses Christopher Todhunter and gets away with it.'

18 'Superlative scheme, Mr Ace, sir.'

19 'On occasion, the psi-scan has been known to be wrong.'

20 'Blue-moon-ish-type planetoid, close to that big bastard with the red spot?'

21 'Where are you spending Christmas, Mr Henry?'

22 'Green slush again. Tut, tut, tut.'

23 'You're absolutely sure there's no way we can kill ourselves?'

24 'Call me Mum-m-m-m-m-my.'

25 'Because, you muffin-making moron, it's not possible.'

26 'I'm gonna send your teeth so far south, you're gonna be flossing through your butt-hole.'

27 'They don't perform any snazzy functions at all?'

28 'I believe you're in my seat, Sonny.'

29 'It's him all right, the obnoxious little gimboid.'

30 'Ugly as my mother.'

31 'Great. Well, that's . . . great. That's really great. What a tricksy piece of software.'

32 'To hell with this. I'm going to loot the shops in the ship's shopping mall.'

33 'Well, looky here, boys. Ol' Sheriff Carton's got hisself all dudded up to die.'

34 'I want to visit strange new worlds, to seek out new life and new civilizations. To boldly go where no person has gone before.'

35 'You never think ahead, you mookle. You're allergic to planning.'

36 'Can't I keep my trousers on for five seconds?'

37 'Buddy, did I do it. I did it so good they're gonna have to redefine the rules of engagement!'

38 'You're going to suggest we surrender, aren't you?'

39 'Sniff your coffee and wake up, Rimmer, we are not friends.'

40 'Hubba–hubba, what have we here?'

41 'Sir, honestly: any bigger and you'll have a balance problem.'

42 'I don't know, you encephalopathetic donkey gonad. Look, dammit!'

43 'We've got no money. Time for you to go hooking.'

44 'Dost thou knoweth who I am?'

45 'Then who the hell's that? Benny Goodman and his Orchestra?'

Crossword 8
'Nanarchy'

The Questions

Across

1 Kochanski got through a whole box of them while watching *Gone with the Wind* (7)

5 What Holly thought had happened to Kryten's face (5,5)

6 Kryten captured the nanobots in one (6)

8 Lister tried to pick this up (4)

9 Popular 20th-century pub game (3-5,6)

11 With boiled eggs (5,8)

14 The crew searched for the planet occupied by these (3,9)

16 The one-armed man (7,6)

20 The nanobots can turn this into food (3,6)

21 The one-armed bandit (7,4)

24 — Nightingdroid (8)

25 Kryten's self-repair system (8)

27 This dude is back and kicking bottom! (5)

Down

2 Weather condition on the planetoid (8,5)

3 He beat the French (4,6)

4 Where Kryten caught the nanobots (7,6)

7 It took Lister 45 minutes to unbutton them (5)

10 The nanobots committed this (6)

12 What Kryten tried to build for Lister (10,3)

13 The grossest thing Kochanski ever heard (4,5)

15 Where the nanobots did their last repair (1,1,1,9)

17 Kryten dunked these for Lister (8)

18 What the planetoid was really (3,5)

19 Would one of these with three legs be ugly? (3,4)

22 Gems made from graphite (8)

23 These can be turned into diamonds (7)

26 The crew's transport on the planetoid (5)

> **'Get my information from the Junior Colour Encyclopaedia of Space. The respect you have for me is awesome, innit?'**
> Holly, 'Queeg'

1 Why did the entire zodiac have to be realigned?
2 What is primordial soup?
3 How far is Neptune from Mimas?
4 According to the particle analyser, what was the planetoid made of?
5 How long did it take the Oblivion virus to hit Cyberia?
6 How had Lister returned to Cyberia?
7 Where were Earth's evacuees rehoused?
8 What was more powerful than the Sun?
9 Which planet had the Leviathan been heading for?
10 How did Kryten suggest they deal with the linkway?
11 Who had a condominium on Venus?
12 What does the duality jump do?
13 Where did Lister's trial take place?
14 What was the North American anti-missile array called?
15 Whereabouts on Lotomi 5 was Cyberia situated?
16 According to Lister, what was used to cover the hole in the Earth's ozone layer?
17 Who had invented the concept of Silicon Heaven?
18 How did Lister jump-start the second 'big bang'?
19 What will the Arre bubble do?

20 How many points did the Mercurian jury award
   Uranus?
21 According to Lister, what is a comet made of?
22 What was Jupiter's 'great red spot'?
23 What is the Omni-Zone?
24 According to Rimmer, what is a time hole?
25 What does the Oblivion virus do?
26 According to Lister, why does all space look familiar?
27 What is the nearest planet to the Sun?
28 How big is 'the' galaxy?
29 After three million years, whose IQ did Holly have?
30 How long had it taken the first virus to eat Kilauea's
   lava lakes?
31 How long had Lister and Krissie been on the Europa
   Testbase?
32 How deep is the lava?
33 What does Holly's CPU control?
34 Which planetoid was only 500 miles across?
35 What was Io's dome made of?
36 What did Lister find Mimas more depressing than?
37 What had happened to the Black Planet?
38 Who owned a holiday cottage on Io?
39 What is it possible to make computer chips out of?
40 How early did *Red Dwarf* break the light barrier?
41 What colour was the Oblivion virus disk?
42 While being sucked into a black hole, if it's Friday 15th
   in the engine room, what is the date in the status room?
43 How far from Earth is the Andromeda Galaxy?
44 What did Holly describe as 'brown trousers time'?
45 What is the speed of light?
46 How many jurors are there on an Arranguu 12 jury?

47 Where was 'South Mars'?

48 Where had the 'Designer' viruses been created?

49 If you cross the road safely in the 'Alpha' universe, what might happen in the 'Omega' universe?

50 What was the viral ident code of the first terraforming virus?

51 What did Holly describe as 'epoch-making'?

52 By how much had the creation of the biosphere been speeded up?

53 How many miles per second is the speed of light?

54 What is the square root of 2049?

55 What was the Plutonian delegation's case against using their planet as a garbage dump?

56 What is the thinking time when stopping at half the speed of light?

57 What's the 'cure' for the solar system?

58 According to Holly, what is the most distinguishing thing about a black hole?

59 Where was John Ewe born and raised?

60 Where had the Pax Vert ejected its putrid load?

61 Which planet was the Martian overspill?

62 Which galaxy did Dr Sabinsky suggest that they move the human race to?

63 How many 'black holes' was *Red Dwarf* 'ambushed' by?

64 According to Lister, what was wrong with Holly's pool shot?

65 How many supernovae did it take to spell out 'COKE ADDS LIFE'?

66 Which planet was the chic-est, most exclusive world in the planetary system?

67 How much is the fine for straying in to Blerion airspace without permission?

68 How long did the crew have to load *Starbug* before *Red Dwarf* was ambushed by the 'black holes'?

69 What does a psi-moon do?

70 What colour was the antidote disk?

71 What is the event horizon of a black hole?

72 How long did it take the eco-accelerator rockets to terraform Rimmerworld?

73 What did Lister liken to Rimmer's Organ Recital night?

74 Where is the Forum of Justice?

75 What does a white hole do?

76 How long before the solar system dies?

Word grid 2

Unscramble the names of famous people featured in *Red Dwarf*, then place them horizontally in the grid. If you have placed them in the correct order the vertical column marked with an arrow will spell out the name of an old acquaintance of Lister's.

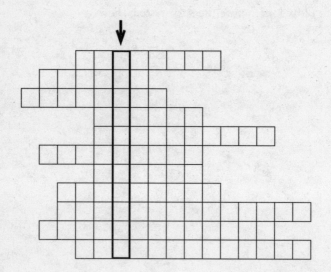

ADHNIG

NUELTALSAR

GTCRHTIAESIAHA

PLOANOEN

STAIPRNU

HYWNEAJON

NOIALONYMREMR

TRLHEI

NYCRTMCAE

TRESHOTERHEAM

NONELN

Number search

The answers to questions 1 to 36 are 'hidden' in the grid below. They may be found arranged vertically, horizontally or diagonally, and even backwards.

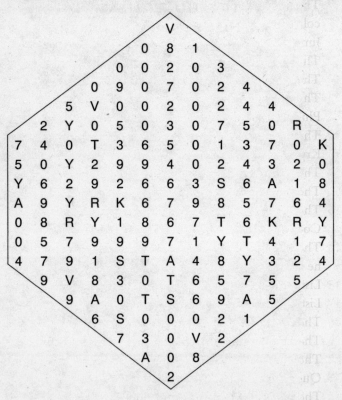

The Questions

1 The speed of light.
2 Lister's *doppelgänger*'s ID code.
3 Starbug's *full* registration number.
4 The number of the stasis booth Rimmer should have got into.
5 The floor on which you would find the Botanical Gardens on the *Enlightenment*.
6 The number of spicy poppadoms taken from the *Nova 5*.
7 The number of zero-gee football magazines in Lister's collection.
8 Jimmy Stewart's honeymoon money.
9 The number of guests at the Rimmers' party.
10 The number of symbols in the cat lexicon.
11 The number of musicians in the New York Philharmonic Orchestra.
12 The time the two Rimmers finally got to bed.
13 Kryten's oblivion passcode.
14 The number of piston towers aboard *Red Dwarf*.
15 The number of gear levers on *Blue Midget*.
16 The number of seats in the Copacabana Hawaiian Cocktail bar.
17 The number of miles Lister was from Liverpool when he first joined *Red Dwarf*.
18 Lister's locker on Mimas Central shuttle station.
19 Lister's address in Bedford Falls.
20 The price of Talkie Toaster.
21 The number of years Rimmer spent on Rimmerworld.
22 The number of days Lister, Kryten and the Cat spent in Quarantine.
23 The vintage of the Château d'Yquem.

24 The number of years that Rimmer was imprisoned by his clones.

25 The number of cats left behind when Frankenstein died.

26 The number of days that Rimmer had 'saved' in stasis.

27 The amount Rimmer had managed to scrimp and scrape together.

28 The APR charged by the Ganymedian Mafia.

29 The year that Lister was born.

30 The cruising speed of *Red Dwarf*.

31 The cost of a shuttle ticket from Mimas to Earth.

32 Flight Co-ordinator McQueen's IQ.

33 The number of selim to Nodnol.

34 The year The Last Chance Saloon was established.

35 The number of episodes of Androids.

36 The number of stars needed to write 'Coke Adds Life'.

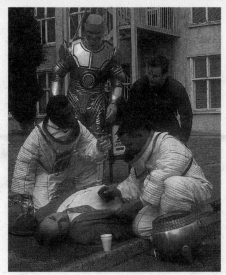

1. How did Rimmer think the man had died?
(Photo: Mike Vaughan)

2. What did Lister of Smeg claim as his prize for beating
the Good Knight? (Photo: Mike Vaughan)

3. Why did Lister award Rimmer a First Officer decoration?
(Photo: Mike Vaughan)

4. Who did Ace rescue from the firing squad?
(Photo: Mike Vaughan)

5. Who did Kryten envisage Kochanski and Lister would invite over for dinner parties? (Photo: Mike Vaughan)

6. According to Kryten, how does Kochanski look at Lister? (Photo: Mike Vaughan)

7. What had Kochanski tried to learn in order to fit in?
(Photo: Mike Vaughan)

8. What had Rimmer 'won' the last time he played the
locker room game? (Photo: Mike Vaughan)

9. Quote: 'Welcome to the Rimmer Experience. A place of wonder, excitement and wonder.' (Photo: Mike Vaughan)

10. What size golf course had Kryten built?
(Photo: Mike Vaughan)

11. Where did Kochanski spend all her time whilst she was at Cyberschool? (Photo: Mike Vaughan)

12. Quote: 'These strides are too tackle-tight, Officer BB. I can barely cruise.' (Photo: Mike Vaughan)

13. Where did Kryten borrow the T72 from?
(Photo: Mike Vaughan)

14. Quote: 'He ain't heavy, sir. He's my brother.'
(Photo: Mike Vaughan)

15. Quote: 'Oh my God, Caroline, you've really let yourself go!'
(Photo: Mike Vaughan)

16. Who has technology way in advance of the crew's?
(Photo: Mike Vaughan)

THE ANSWERS

References are provided in brackets following certain sections of the Answers. These refer either to episodes of *Red Dwarf* (e.g. 'Backwards', 'Meltdown') or to the *Red Dwarf* novels (i.e. *Red Dwarf: Infinity Welcomes Careful Drivers*, shortened here to *Infinity*; *Better Than Life*; *Last Human*; *Backwards*; and *The Red Dwarf Omnibus*, shortened to *Omnibus*), all published by Penguin Books. Page numbers for *Last Human* and *Backwards* are from the hardback editions. In some cases two references are given (one to an episode and one to a novel), and sometimes, just to complicate things, there are two different answers to a single question.

Staircase 1

'Glory or insanity awaits!'

1 His anxiety chip goes into overdrive. ('Backwards')
2 Abraham Lincoln. ('Meltdown')
3 Duane Dibbley. ('Emohawk – Polymorph II')
4 Lister. ('Balance of Power')
5 The red switch. ('The Last Day')
6 Arsehole. ('Kryten')
7 Shrank the Good Knight's horse. ('Stoke Me a Clipper')
8 Black. ('Dimension Jump')
9 Zippo. ('Epideme')
10 Petersen. ('The End')
11 The Hacienda Space Bar on Miranda. ('Marooned')
12 Someplace near Uruguay. ('Confidence and Paranoia')
13 It corrupts mechanoids' circuit boards. ('Beyond a Joke')
14 Xanadu. ('Timeslides')
15 Eight feet across. ('Tikka to Ride')
16 5.05 a.m. ('Me^2')
17 A little food, as much water as they could carry and that magnetic fishing game. ('Duct Soup')
18 'She's Out of My Life'. ('Marooned')
19 The Sixties. ('Parallel Universe')
20 Tights, bras, skimpy vests and little socks. ('Blue')
21 They came back as someone's skiing holiday. ('Timeslides')
22 Continue the discussion. ('Balance of Power')
23 The next time Lister ran into his wife. ('Ouroboros')
24 His day-glo orange moon boots. ('Kryten')

25 A mirror. ('Balance of Power')

26 Twelve hours. ('Marooned')

27 Kryten's negadrive energy. ('Beyond a Joke')

28 Two thousand and two. ('White Hole')

29 Cloister (or Clister). ('Waiting for God')

30 Near Mount Sinai. ('Better Than Life')

31 Lister and Chen. ('Confidence and Paranoia')

32 The doors. ('Duct Soup')

33 The Duke of Lincoln. ('Timeslides')

34 It was too radical, too unconventional, too mould-breaking for the examiners to accept. ('The End')

35 £10,000. ('Backwards')

36 Pawn sacrifice. ('Meltdown')

37 A monkey wrench. ('Beyond a Joke')

38 To go into Kochanski's quarters and wallow in self-pity. ('Confidence and Paranoia')

39 Lister keyed in the correct security code using the luck virus. ('Quarantine')

40 In Bonn. ('Better Than Life')

41 The Texas Book Depository. ('Tikka to Ride')

42 Lister's socks. ('Me²')

43 Kryten. ('White Hole')

44 A+ distinction. ('Waiting for God')

45 Rimmer. ('The Inquisitor')

46 Three thousand. ('Stoke Me a Clipper')

47 He confiscated a quarter of a cigarette. ('Balance of Power')

48 £50. ('Backwards')

49 Colostomy Explosion. ('Beyond a Joke')

50 Staff Colonel Count Von Stauffenberg. ('Timeslides')

51 Until lunchtime. ('Justice')

52 Biscuit, custard, ink and general dirty marks. ('Waiting for God')

53 People who break into lockers deserve everything they get, you cheap, double-crossing slime-ball. ('Blue')

54 Sebastian Doyle. ('Back to Reality')

55 Rather striking. ('Me²')

56 A toilet duck. ('Epideme')

57 *Biggles Learns to Fly*. ('Marooned')

58 Because of a volcanic eruption. ('The End')

59 Mr Flibble. ('Quarantine')

60 A snake eating its own tail. ('Ouroboros')

61 Half-wit, hopeless, hideous failure. ('Holoship')

62 An apple of the people. ('Back to Reality')

63 Three hours. ('The End')

64 Latrines and the three o'clock watch every morning. ('Balance of Power')

65 Rimmer. ('Dimension Jump')

66 Lizzie and Jane. ('Beyond a Joke')

67 Eight months. ('Waiting for God')

68 Lister. ('Camille')

69 Sixteen. ('Holoship')

70 The Legendary DuBois Brothers. ('Marooned')

71 Lister. ('White Hole')

72 Idlewild. ('Tikka to Ride')

73 With massive whips. ('Waiting for God')

74 Dead men's boots. ('Holoship')

75 To outrank Rimmer. ('Balance of Power')

76 Eight. ('Justice')

77 22 November 1963, Dallas. ('Tikka to Ride')

78 One hundred and twenty-three. ('The End')

79 Higher up. ('Tikka to Ride')

The Answers

80 Neutron bomb juggling. ('Demons and Angels')
81 A photograph of his mother. ('Me²')
82 For keeping him sane. ('Stoke Me a Clipper')
83 When he attended inspection parade during his
    journey to 'Trip Out City'. ('Stasis Leak')
84 Rimmer. ('Blue')
85 They wear protective herbs. ('Demons and Angels')
86 Thirty-nine. ('The End')
87 Lister. ('Epideme')
88 In the middle of the floor. ('Me²')
89 A Texan tourist. ('The Last Day')
90 Mr Flibble. ('Quarantine')
91 Holly's decimalized musical note. ('Kryten', or *Infinity*
    p. 168)
92 When Lister's safety harness snapped and he fell into
    the cargo bay. ('Balance of Power')
93 Five hundred. ('The Inquisitor')
94 Two hundred and seventy thousand, seven hundred
    and twenty-five to one. ('Quarantine')
95 Less than twenty minutes. ('Demons and Angels')
96 Lister. ('Legion')
97 Three. ('Tikka to Ride')
98 He was a prat. ('White Hole')
99 A night and a day in the bed of the Queen of
    Camelot. ('Stoke Me a Clipper')
100 Five, including a wrong number. ('The Last Day')
101 3.4 inches. ('Epideme')
102 In the library. ('Future Echoes')
103 Lister himself. ('Ouroboros')
104 The right of the POW to non-violent constraint.
    ('Gunmen of the Apocalypse')

Crossword 1
'Backwards'

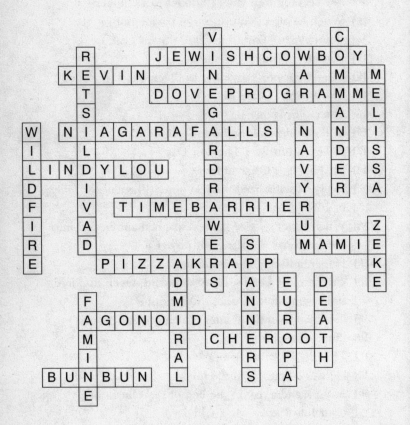

'I've forgotten what I was going to say!'

1 Kryten. ('Backwards')
2 Lister. ('Duct Soup')
3 Holly. ('Confidence and Paranoia')
4 Lister. ('Epideme')
5 Lister. ('Back to Reality')
6 Cat. ('Ouroboros')
7 Lister. ('Tikka to Ride')
8 Rimmer. ('Future Echoes')
9 Rimmer. ('Stoke Me a Clipper')
10 Lister in Rimmer's body. ('Bodyswap')
11 Lister. ('Nanarchy')
12 Rimmer. ('Balance of Power')
13 Kryten. ('Ouroboros')
14 Rimmer. ('Demons and Angels')
15 Cat. ('Dimension Jump')
16 Lister. ('Better Than Life')
17 Rimmer. ('Back to Reality')
18 Lister. ('Blue')
19 Cat. ('Confidence and Paranoia')
20 Mechanoid Camille. ('Camille')
21 Lister. ('Beyond a Joke')
22 Lister ('Me²')
23 Cat. ('Back to Reality')
24 Holly. ('Demons and Angels')
25 Rimmer. ('Dimension Jump')
26 Kryten. ('Blue')
27 Rimmer in Lister's body. ('Bodyswap')
28 Cat. ('The Inquisitor')

29 Cat. ('Nanarchy')
30 Ace's computer. ('Dimension Jump')
31 Epideme. ('Epideme')
32 Kryten. ('DNA')
33 Cat. ('The End')
34 Talkie Toaster. ('Future Echoes')
35 Kochanski. ('Ouroboros')
36 Rimmer. ('Holoship')
37 Kryten. ('Duct Soup')
38 Cat. ('Confidence and Paranoia')
39 Lister. ('Stoke Me a Clipper')
40 Rimmer. ('Tikka to Ride')
41 Lister. ('The Inquisitor')
42 Rimmer self-loathing. ('Terrorform')
43 Cat. ('Beyond a Joke')
44 Backwards cyclist. ('Backwards')
45 Holly. ('Thanks for the Memory')
46 Kryten. ('Epideme')
47 Blaze Falconburger. ('Timeslides')
48 Rimmer. ('Balance of Power')
49 Lister. ('Blue')
50 Lister. ('Justice')
51 Rimmer. ('Kryten', or *Infinity* p. 170)
52 Kryten. ('White Hole')
53 Kochanski. ('Nanarchy')
54 Cat. ('Kryten', or *Infinity* p. 188)
55 Lister. ('The Last Day')
56 Cat. ('Legion')
57 Rimmer. ('Marooned')
58 Cat. ('Me^2')
59 Cat. ('Tikka to Ride')

60 Holly. ('Meltdown')
61 Rimmer. ('Stoke Me a Clipper')
62 Rimmer. ('Waiting for God')
63 Lister. ('Out of Time')
64 Cat. ('Blue')
65 Hilly. ('Parallel Universe')
66 Lister. ('Polymorph')
67 Kochanski. ('Beyond a Joke')
68 Derelict ship's black box recording. ('Psirens')
69 Cat. ('Duct Soup')
70 Lister. ('Waiting for God')
71 Cat. ('Kryten', or *Infinity* p. 175)
72 Cat. ('Quarantine')
73 Kochanski. ('Duct Soup')
74 Holly. ('Queeg')
75 Lister. ('Rimmerworld')
76 Rimmer. ('Blue')
77 Captain Hollister. ('Stasis Leak')
78 Holly. ('Terrorform')
79 Holly. ('Thanks for the Memory')
80 Kryten. ('Beyond a Joke')
81 Rimmer. ('Timeslides')
82 Lister. ('Waiting for God')
83 Kryten. ('Nanarchy')
84 Rimmer. ('White Hole')
85 Cat. ('Epideme')
86 Spare Head Three. ('DNA')
87 Todhunter. ('The End')
88 Lister. ('Nanarchy')
89 Cat. ('Psirens')
90 Lister. ('Waiting for God')

91 Captain Voorhese. ('Stoke Me a Clipper')
92 Kryten. ('Quarantine')
93 *Centauri* simulant. ('Beyond a Joke')

'Not all the way through, no, but I can quote some though'

1 Cat. (*Last Human* p. 41)
2 Cat. (*Better Than Life* p. 202)
3 Rimmer's dad. (*Infinity* p. 283)
4 Lister. (*Last Human* p. 230)
5 Rimmer. (*Last Human* p. 98)
6 Rimmer. (*Backwards* p. 302)
7 Michael McGruder. (*Last Human* p. 272)
8 Rimmer. (*Backwards* p. 26)
9 Kryten. (*Better Than Life* p. 201)
10 Spanners. (*Backwards* p. 99)
11 Talkie Toaster. (*Better Than Life* p. 226)
12 Rimmer. (*Backwards* p. 232)
13 Lister. (*Last Human* p. 167)
14 Rimmer. (*Backwards* p. 200)
15 Rimmer. (*Backwards* p. 44)
16 Rimmer. (*Backwards* p. 58)
17 Tonto Jitterman. (*Better Than Life* p. 67)
18 Admiral Peter Tranter. (*Backwards* p. 126)
19 Kryten. (*Infinity* p. 198)
20 Ace Rimmer. (*Backwards* p. 208)

21 Will Carton. (*Backwards* p. 293)
22 Spanners. (*Backwards* p. 111)
23 Cat. (*Last Human* p. 73)
24 Lister. (*Backwards* p. 186)
25 Rimmer's duplicate. (*Infinity* p. 239)
26 Spanners. (*Backwards* p. 90)
27 Rimmer. (*Better Than Life* p. 4)
28 Cat. (*Backwards* p. 155)
29 Cat. (*Backwards* p. 324)
30 Cat. (*Backwards* p. 335)
31 Kochanski. (*Infinity* p. 68)
32 Lister. (*Backwards* p. 311)
33 Lister. (*Infinity* p. 34)
34 Cat. (*Backwards* p. 330)
35 Rimmer as Trixie LaBouche. (*Better Than Life* p. 24)
36 Kochanski. (*Last Human* p. 143)
37 Rimmer. (*Last Human* p. 204)
38 Lister. (*Backwards* p. 177)
39 Lister. (*Backwards* p. 159)
40 George McIntyre. (*Infinity* p. 26)
41 Lister. (*Better Than Life* p. 209)
42 Lister's *doppelgänger*. (*Last Human* p. 196)
43 The computer on the *Nova 5*. (*Infinity* p. 164)
44 Avril Dupont. (*Better Than Life* p. 130)
45 Rimmer. (*Better Than Life* p. 14)
46 Lister. (*Infinity* p. 177)

Word search 1
The *Dwarf*

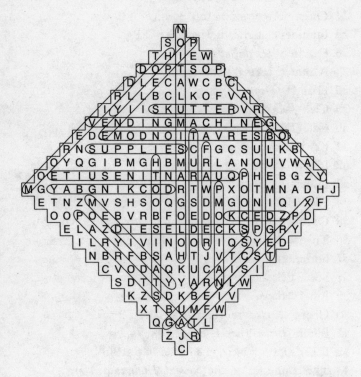

'Head!'

1 Over fourteen million. ('Balance of Power')
2 One. ('The End')
3 Onion deprivation. (*Backwards* p. 144)
4 A cheap razor. ('Nanarchy')
5 H and J (woh and boh). ('Kryten', or *Infinity* p. 168)
6 That they had abolished war, cured all disease and got rid of those little western saloon doors you get in trendy clothes shops. ('Balance of Power')
7 It's like a cock-up only much, much bigger. ('Parallel Universe')
8 'Well, it's a laugh, innit?' ('Waiting for God')
9 Over a decade. (*Backwards* p. 144)
10 The friendship he shares with his collection of singing potatoes. ('Queeg')
11 Somewhere along the habitation decks. ('Polymorph')
12 About three million years. ('Better Than Life')
13 His punctuation. ('Waiting for God')
14 Because it was lead-lined. ('Justice')
15 It had been 'alf-inched. ('Thanks for the Memory')
16 98%. ('Me²')
17 A bucketful of sheep's slop. ('Confidence and Paranoia')
18 The cello. ('Kryten', or *Infinity* p. 168)
19 3.41 minutes. ('White Hole')
20 Because it happened to be the face of the greatest and most prolific lover who ever lived. ('Balance of Power')

Word search 2
'Stoke Me a Clipper'

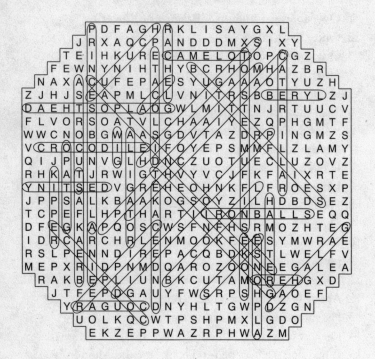

'Ippy dippy, my space shippy . . .'

1 Eight. (*Better Than Life* p. 5)
2 Aboard the *Gemini 12*. ('Tikka to Ride')
3 STA 7676-45-327-28V. (*Last Human* p. 37)
4 In *Blue Midget*. ('Kryten', or *Infinity* p. 185)
5 It didn't freeze time completely, it just slowed it down by 95%. (*Last Human* p. 48)
6 The *Mayflower*. (*Last Human* p. 206)
7 There had been a mutiny *en route*. (*Last Human* p. 148)
8 Six weeks. ('Backwards')
9 The SSS *Esperanto*. (Nanarchy)
10 Four and a half years. (*Infinity* p. 40)
11 Less than fifteen minutes. (*Backwards* p. 92)
12 After every ten thousand years. (*Last Human* p. 182)
13 A light alloy. ('White Hole')
14 Plexiglas. (*Backwards* p. 180)
15 Through the service ducts. ('Duct Soup')
16 Twelve. (*Infinity* p. 186)
17 It had fallen through a wormhole into the Omni-Zone, and been ejected into a new dimension of reality. (*Last Human* p. 186)
18 The *Enlightenment*. ('Holoship')
19 Pig offal. (*Better Than Life* p. 173)
20 One hundred and twenty. (*Last Human* p. 208)
21 A Reliant Robin. ('Better Than Life')
22 Either they were under attack or the baked potatoes were burning. ('Blue')
23 *Starbug 2*. ('Backwards')
24 Two, perhaps three months. (*Infinity* p. 208)

25 The *Lagos*. (*Last Human* p. 42)

26 $£30 billion. (*Backwards* p. 109)

27 It had major flight design flaws. ('Holoship')

28 Six months. (*Infinity* p. 161)

29 Two thousand six hundred. (*Better Than Life* p. 100)

30 A tandem. ('Backwards')

31 *Starbug*'s service ducts. ('Duct Soup')

32 Behind a woman clutching a baby. ('Dimension Jump')

33 Made a subatomic version and turned the rest of the atoms into a planetoid for safe keeping. ('Nanarchy')

34 The location of the derelict starship *Mayflower*. (*Last Human* p. 147)

35 Zero mass. ('Holoship')

36 Eight. (*Last Human* p. 182)

37 Four thousand, six hundred and eighty. (*Better Than Life* p. 93)

38 Three days before it set off. (*Backwards* p. 86)

39 Twelve. ('Psirens')

40 In a safe back on *Starbug*. (*Last Human* p. 70)

41 Three. (*Backwards* p. 51)

42 A Jeep with a swivel-mounted rocket-launcher. (*Last Human* p. 136)

43 Midnight. (*Backwards* p. 19)

44 A rusty nail. (*Backwards* p. 43)

45 An Oldsmobile. (*Better Than Life* p. 71)

46 The *Leviathan*, a 23rd-century JMC supply ship. ('Epideme')

47 Forever onwards. ('Waiting for God')

48 In the hold. (*Backwards* p. 46)

49 Almost 400 miles. (*Last Human* p. 206)

50 A cutting tool. (*Backwards* p. 67)

51 The *A to Z of Mimas*. (*Infinity* p. 15)

52 Every four hours. ('Duct Soup')

53 The prototype craft. (*Backwards* p. 89)

54 A seriously high-powered heat-seeking missile.
   (*Backwards* p. 157)

55 Ferry ore from ship to surface. (*Backwards* p. 178)

56 Twelve years. (*Backwards* p. 75)

57 About three weeks. (*Better Than Life* p. 92)

58 Three hundred and seventy nine. (*Backwards* p. 179)

59 In a hillside cave. (*Backwards* p. 45)

60 To terraform a planet in the Andromeda Galaxy. (*Last Human* p. 148)

61 Docking bay 475. (*Backwards* p. 335)

62 At a busy rank back at Mimas Central. (*Infinity* p. 15)

63 Twenty-five minutes. (*Infinity* p. 36)

64 Three hundred and fifty thousand years. (*Infinity* p. 132)

65 The code-name for the prototype craft that could break
   the light barrier. (*Backwards* p. 86)

66 In the Pacific. (*Last Human* p. 162)

67 Skew-whiff in the ornamental gardens of the Palace of
   Versailles. (*Better Than Life* p. 3)

68 Because they were carrying too much weight. ('Blue')

69 Most ice cream vans. ('Beyond a Joke')

Crossword 2
'Thanks for the Memory'

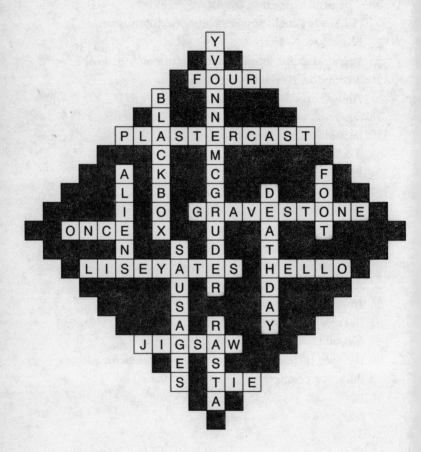

The Answers

'Did someone just turn over two pages at once?'

1 Nobby Nobody. (*Better Than Life* p. 35)
2 Strange people. People who don't like other people. Not polite, besuited second-hand car salespeople. Hermit-type inbred people, with criss-crossed front teeth and a penchant for stews well stocked with human flesh. (*Backwards* p. 39)
3 A huge maggot farm. (*Infinity* p. 265)
4 Peter Pessimism. (*Backwards* p. 302)
5 Three toilets lashed together, covered with bin liners stuffed with vacuum cleaner fluff. (*Better Than Life* p. 166)
6 Through the mouth and ears. (*Last Human* p. 234)
7 Death. (*Backwards* p. 322)
8 A rusty bottle-opener he'd found in the sink. (*Last Human* p. 85)
9 Bull Heinman. (*Better Than Life* p. 54)
10 Einstein. (*Better Than Life* p. 3)
11 For two reasons: (a) sentimental; (b) they were just the thing for opening bottles of beer. (*Infinity* p. 111)
12 Because he's a coward, so he's permanently scared. (*Backwards* p. 325)
13 3454H. (*Last Human* p. 171)
14 Lister's *doppelgänger*. (*Last Human* p. 193)
15 Ace Rimmer. (*Backwards* p. 228)
16 Solidgram International. (*Better Than Life* p. 44)
17 Van Gogh. (*Infinity* p. 248)
18 Lister's *doppelgänger*. (*Last Human* p. 130)

19 Androids and getting a new squeegee mop. (*Infinity* p. 215)

20 For embezzling funds from the Miranda Insurance Company. (*Last Human* p. 195)

21 Bert. (*Better Than Life* p. 8)

22 Start wars. (*Last Human* p. 16)

23 For the best part of twenty years. (*Better Than Life* p. 127)

24 Five. (*Last Human* p. 87)

25 For his entire suit collection. (*Backwards* p. 333)

26 One dollarpound. (*Infinity* p. 24)

27 Six months suspended. (*Better Than Life* p. 174)

28 A piece of paper with galactic coordinates on it. (*Last Human* p. 142)

29 Holly. (*Backwards* p. 176)

30 Committee for the Liberation and Integration of Terrifying Organisms for their Rehabilitation Into Society. (*Better Than Life* p. 207)

31 By killing other life forms better than anyone else. (*Last Human* p. 244)

32 Rimmer's mum. (*Backwards* p. 167)

33 The toothpaste. (*Infinity* p. 171)

34 Because they all thought they were God's gift to soldiering. (*Last Human* p. 211)

35 Jasmine. (*Better Than Life* p. 165)

36 Pink. (*Last Human* p. 121)

37 Five thousand. (*Infinity* p. 272)

38 Down at the drugstore. (*Better Than Life* p. 10)

39 Cat. (*Backwards* p. 52)

40 The genome for all DNA. (*Last Human* p. 149)

41 Nine seconds. (*Infinity* p. 150)

42 Lister. (*Last Human* p. 12)

43 Ten o'clock. (*Backwards* p. 12)

44 A sealed foil tray of chicken vindaloo, two spicy poppadoms and an onion salad, three six-packs of Leopard lager and Lister's one and only photograph of Kristine Kochanski. (*Better Than Life* p. 217)

45 Rimmer. (*Last Human* p. 42)

46 Five and a half hours. (*Backwards* p. 51)

47 Every single stock market had crashed simultaneously. (*Better Than Life* p. 26)

48 Fifteen minutes. (*Infinity* p. 228)

49 Dicky Duckworth. (*Backwards* p. 169)

50 A chicken. (*Last Human* p. 215)

51 Thirty-two. (*Better Than Life* p. 35)

52 He performed his famous impersonation of a whippet with a sphincter full of dynamite. (*Backwards* p. 61)

53 French. (*Better Than Life* p. 130)

54 Peter Tranter. (*Backwards* p. 84)

55 Corridor 1: gamma 755. (*Infinity* p. 77)

56 Tokyo. (*Last Human* p. 154)

57 A tyre lever. (*Backwards* p. 65)

58 One hundred and seventy-one. (*Better Than Life* p. 108)

59 Five months. (*Last Human* p. 167)

60 Four. (*Infinity* p. 227)

61 The Cat. (*Backwards* p. 159)

62 Yvonne McGruder. (*Last Human* p. 272)

63 Eight inches. (*Better Than Life* p. 24)

64 The Albanian State Washing Machine Company. (*Last Human* p. 61)

65 In Lister's fishtank. (*Infinity* p. 112)

66 Billy-Joe Epstein's. (*Backwards* p. 79)

67 Doug Naylor. (*Last Human* p. i.)

68 His one and only dress shirt – two collar sizes too small
   – and a yellow kipper tie with a woman in birthing
   stirrups motif, and nicely pressed cream slacks. (*Last
   Human* p. 10)

69 W C. (*Backwards* p. 186)

70 His top one hundred. (*Better Than Life* p. 160)

71 In the docking bay. (*Infinity* p. 169)

72 Two thousand. (*Last Human* p. 231)

73 The musical toilet-roll dispenser. (*Better Than Life*
   p. 147)

74 12th Street on Triton. (*Last Human* p. 164)

75 Due to extraordinary length of his weapon. (*Backwards*
   p. 174)

76 Blue. (*Better Than Life* p. 38)

77 In a microdot, occupying the dot of the 'i' on page
   three. (*Infinity* p. 54)

78 Six. (*Last Human* p. 79)

79 Because he couldn't make the payments on his body
   mortgage. (*Better Than Life* p. 51)

80 Admiral Peter Tranter. (*Backwards* p. 84)

81 Eleven to four. (*Last Human* p. 301)

82 Lister's. (*Last Human* p. 23)

83 Under the bunks after Kryten had tidied Lister's
   sleeping quarters. (*Infinity* p. 214)

84 Orange. (*Last Human* p. 232)

85 The Death Wheel. (*Backwards* p. 222)

86 Jimmy, Tonto and Rimmer. (*Better Than Life* p. 62)

87 Europe. (*Better Than Life* p. 131)

88 Purple. (*Last Human* p. 39)

89 Eight years. (*Backwards* p. 16)

90 A hologram's 'H'. (*Infinity* p. 27)

91 Twenty. (*Better Than Life* p. 17)

92 Pherson. (*Backwards* p. 114)

93 Yellow sandstone. (*Last Human* p. 75)

94 Better Than Life. (*Infinity* p. 18)

95 The best part of five weeks. (*Better Than Life* p. 226)

96 Richard, Joe and Matthew. (*Last Human* p. v)

97 Lewis Pemberton. (*Backwards* p. 119)

98 Seven. (*Last Human* p. 309)

99 Because he had taken the luck virus and he wanted the Rage to choose him. The luck virus made your dreams come true. (*Last Human* p. 292)

100 Rimmer. (*Backwards* p. 136)

101 (a) Never wear diamonds before lunch, and (b) with cutlery, start from the outside and work your way in. (*Infinity* p. 253)

102 At least ninety minutes. (*Backwards* p. 52)

103 In the penal colony known as Cyberia on Lotomi 5. (*Last Human* p. 79)

104 Every silly bastard gets a vote. (*Backwards* p. 176)

105 I think, therefore I am. (*Infinity* p. 28)

106 Lister. (*Last Human* p. 298)

107 $£30 million. (*Better Than Life* p. 26)

108 Michael Longman. (*Last Human* p. 157)

109 Purple. (*Better Than Life* p. 81)

110 Mr Capote's. (*Last Human* p. 83)

111 S.M.A.K.I.B.B.F.B. – Smoke me a kipper, I'll be back for breakfast. (*Last Human* p. 305)

112 Spazzies, durnoids and thickies. (*Backwards* p. 5)

113 Through the oxygeneration outlet pipe. (*Last Human* p. 283)

114 Yellow. (*Backwards* p. 32)
115 Three hours. (*Infinity* p. 79)
116 Sewage. (*Better Than Life* p. 127)

Staircase 2

G	U	I	T	A	R
N	O	D	N	O	L
N	O	R	W	E	B
P	A	D	D	L	E
H	E	C	T	O	R
H	U	D	Z	E	N

'What a guy!'

1 Howard. (*Backwards* p. 88)
2 By dislocating both his shoulders and popping them behind his ears, then slipping between the ropes. ('Stoke Me a Clipper')
3 Ace. ('Dimension Jump')
4 Billy-Joe Epstein. (*Backwards* p. 91)
5 Forty knots. ('Dimension Jump')
6 Become the next Ace Rimmer. ('Stoke Me a Clipper')

 7 Basic training in the Space Corps Special Service. (*Backwards* p. 229)

 8 He caught the business end of a neutron tank. ('Stoke Me a Clipper')

 9 An altercation with a door jamb. (*Backwards* p. 105)

10 Little Tommy's. ('Dimension Jump')

11 On Europa. (*Backwards* p. 113)

12 Follow his coffin. ('Stoke Me a Clipper')

13 Heroes' welcomes with twenty-one-gun salutes in front of the entire Admiralty. ('Dimension Jump')

14 Cheroots. (*Backwards* p. 105)

15 Nineteen hundred hours. ('Dimension Jump')

16 His right. (*Backwards* p. 88)

17 Commander. ('Dimension Jump')

18 An ice-skater's friend. ('Stoke Me a Clipper')

19 A holiday cottage on Io. (*Backwards* p. 124)

20 Twelve hours, maybe less. ('Stoke Me a Clipper')

21 Ace. ('Dimension Jump')

22 It was a trophy from the Academy boxing finals in his second year. (*Backwards* p. 88)

23 The freedom the cockpit of speed gave him. (*Backwards* p. 113)

24 Astrocuts. ('Stoke Me a Clipper')

Staircase 3

V	A	L	K	Y	R	I	E
S	I	M	U	L	A	N	T
L	A	N	S	T	R	O	M
D	A	N	D	R	U	F	F
B	U	L	G	A	R	I	A
P	A	R	A	L	L	E	L
N	A	P	O	L	E	O	N
G	A	Z	P	A	C	H	O

'Dormouse cheeks!'

1 Eighty-four. ('The End')
2 Fatboy. ('Beyond a Joke')
3 The E string. ('Quarantine')
4 Mimas. ('Ouroboros')
5 Being handsome and wonderful. ('Dimension Jump')
6 Don't eat greasy food. ('Balance of Power')
7 An old retro housing. ('Duct Soup')
8 Four. ('Thanks for the Memory')
9 He can think and play the guitar. ('Epideme')
10 The Bahamas. ('Timeslides')
11 The 22nd century. ('Tikka to Ride')
12 The manager of the London Jets. ('Confidence and Paranoia')
13 The entire room. ('Justice')

14 Three. ('Epideme')

15 Three. ('The End')

16 They eat and sleep. ('DNA')

17 By failing all his exams and applying. ('Kryten')

18 When he swore to Rimmer that he'd never mention gazpacho soup again. ('Me^2')

19 Because he can't grow a big moustache. ('Duct Soup')

20 Eight months. ('Thanks for the Memory')

21 The right. ('Kryten', or *Infinity* p. 178)

22 Goebbels. ('Meltdown')

23 Because his right arm does all his favourite things. ('Epideme')

24 Because he didn't want to get tied down to a career. ('Waiting for God')

25 Forty-five minutes. ('Nanarchy')

26 A petrol pump. ('Thanks for the Memory')

27 As a git. ('Justice')

28 One cigarette for every day that he obeyed him. ('Balance of Power')

29 Geography. ('Backwards')

30 In the middle of the Bootle Players' amateur production of *The Importance of Being Earnest*. ('Duct Soup')

Word search 3
Non-human life forms

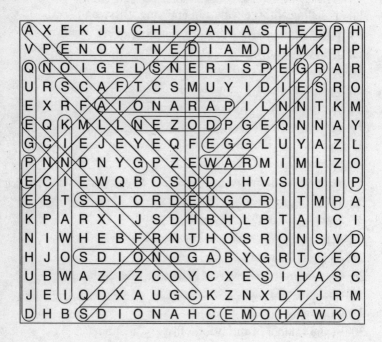

'When I finally get round to writing my Good Psycho Guide, this place is gonna get raves'

1 Desires and longings. (Better Than Life p. 20)
2 In a souvenir shop on the Uranian moon of Miranda.
   (*Better Than Life* p. 32)

3 By tapping on the jamjar with a pencil. ('Nanarchy')

4 Close to a thousand years. (*Last Human* p. 11)

5 By plug-in scramble cards. (*Backwards* p. 192)

6 Twice. ('Justice')

7 Projectile vomiting. (*Last Human* p. 16)

8 *Red Dwarf*'s back-up computer. ('Queeg')

9 A giant hog. (*Backwards* p. 53)

10 2X4C. ('Beyond a Joke')

11 A huge sofa. (*Last Human* p. 173)

12 Because emotions aren't built into their software. ('Better Than Life')

13 A pleasure Gelf. ('Camille')

14 Because he works better with an identity. ('Blue')

15 Because of his capacity for invention and design. (*Backwards* p. 224)

16 Gary. ('Kryten')

17 M'Aiden Ty-One. (*Backwards* p. 192)

18 93.75%. ('Camille')

19 Twenty-five miles an hour. (*Better Than Life* p. 200)

20 On Blerios 15. (*Last Human* p. 55)

21 Loretta. ('Gunmen of the Apocalypse')

22 Because he's more lenient towards mechanicals. (*Last Human* p. 74)

23 Almost forty years. ('Rimmerworld')

24 Kryten. ('The Inquisitor')

25 Six feet six. (*Last Human* p. 95)

26 They just had to stop moving. ('Nanarchy')

27 The Penthouse Suite on A deck. ('Camille')

28 Seven. (*Backwards* p. 193)

29 Earth. ('Polymorph')

30 Just above his right eyebrow. (*Last Human* p. 174)

31 Two feet. ('Kryten')

32 Two thin steel ashtrays. (*Better Than Life* p. 180)

33 Gelfs. ('Beyond a Joke')

34 A simple one-piece cotton robe. (*Last Human* p. 66)

35 Because he's a Pisces and she's part smegging hippopotamus! (*Last Human* p. 96)

36 His replacement eye, a fine pair of back-up ears and an extremely useful spare heart. (*Backwards* p. 195)

37 It closed its own gills and suffocated in water. ('Back to Reality')

38 Epideme. ('Epideme')

39 The Cyberian guards. (*Last Human* p. 109)

40 On the landing gantry. ('The Last Day')

41 So no single species would have sole access to the *Mayflower*. (*Last Human* p. 149)

42 Gordon. ('Better Than Life')

43 A polymorph that's been spayed at birth and half-domesticated. It's been trained to change its shape at its owner's behest. ('Emohawk – Polymorph II')

44 A symbi-morph. (*Last Human* p. 170)

45 A chainsaw. ('The Inquisitor')

46 The Dingotang called Deki. (*Last Human* p. 176)

47 Albert. ('Kryten')

48 Able. ('Beyond a Joke')

49 A black-and-white, lightly matrixed humanoid shape. (*Last Human* p. 177)

50 Break objects down into their component atoms then recombine those atoms to repair damaged circuits. ('Nanarchy')

51 The double-threaded wing nut. (*Better Than Life* p. 86)

52 An empty simulant unit. (*Last Human* p. 185)

53 One, take it on and kill it and, two, run away. ('Polymorph')

54 Creepers. (*Last Human* p. 65)

55 An Alberog. (*Last Human* p. 11)

56 Mindless pap. ('Camille')

57 Frank. ('Blue')

58 Because they were only bonded with one hook. (*Last Human* p. 221)

59 By sawing off the top of his skull with a blunt blade and slowly spooning out his brains before his eyes, while simultaneously kicking him in the gonads with a steel-capped boot until they were pulped to a mush resembling, in colour and consistency, boysenberry jam. Or, ripping off his limbs one by one and buggering him to death with the soggy end of his right arm. Or, splitting open his stomach with a pair of rusty scissors, force feeding him with his own spleen, liver, pancreas and kidneys, raw, then tugging out his bowels and holding them over his face until the offal worked its way through what was left of his digestive system, and drowning him in his own crap! (*Backwards* pp. 194–5)

60 Forty. ('Justice')

61 They roamed the plains of the desert asteroids and bartered with the Gelf communities for emotions and memories, which they then sold to simulants for vast profit. (*Last Human* p. 90)

62 The goat. (*Last Human* p. 254)

63 In a plane crash. (*Infinity* p. 182)

64 A Potent and a member of the Blerion High Council. (*Last Human* p. 64)

65 Levi jeans, whisky, VCRs and sperm. (*Last Human* p. 89)

66 A floral nightdress and a lace-trimmed cap. (*Backwards* p. 53)

67 Forty. (*Better Than Life* p. 95)

68 To use as a guinea pig for a technique called Intelligence Compression. ('White Hole')

69 A rabbit. (*Backwards* p. 136)

70 About twenty seconds. ('Beyond a Joke')

71 A mile across. ('Emohawk – Polymorph II')

72 Agonoids. (*Backwards* p. 190)

73 Three weeks. ('Gunmen of the Apocalypse')

74 The simulants. (*Last Human* p. 183)

75 Eyes. (*Backwards* p. 192)

76 They have to judge themselves. ('The Inquisitor')

77 For doing revolting things to a yak. (*Last Human* p. 79)

78 It secreted a venom, a poison, possibly even a hallucinogenic. ('Back to Reality')

79 Someone you hadn't killed yet. (*Backwards* p. 193)

80 Confidence and Paranoia. ('Confidence and Paranoia')

81 By throwing his own right leg at him. (*Last Human* p. 115)

82 A crossbow. ('Back to Reality')

83 They have the same motherboard. ('Beyond a Joke')

84 Bits of DNA grizzle. (*Last Human* p. 16)

85 In the engine room. ('Psirens')

86 Djuhn 'Keep. (*Backwards* p. 224)

87 One hundred degrees. ('Meltdown')

88 McCartney. ('Future Echoes', or *Infinity* p. 112)

89 Fourteen months. ('Queeg')

90 The skutters. ('Better Than Life')

91 In a Star Corps Medical Engineer. ('Epideme')

92 Emotions. ('Polymorph')

93 A goat, a cobra and a leopard. (*Last Human* p. 251)

94 Because there was nothing new to explore in his body. ('Nanarchy')

95 Back to front and upside down. ('Bodyswap')

96 To be everyone's perfect companion. ('Camille')

97 When he'd last cleaned out the salad tray of his fridge. (*Last Human* p. 16)

98 With limpet mines. ('Back to Reality')

99 Otrozone. ('Beyond a Joke')

100 5%. ('Holoship')

101 He expunges them. ('The Inquisitor')

102 Because the manufacturers hadn't considered it cost-effective to fit them with belief chips. (*Better Than Life* p. 86)

103 Seventy-four. (*Backwards* p. 192)

104 The Mystics 'saw' them. (*Last Human* p. 79)

105 The storage bay. ('The Inquisitor')

106 To be the first to set foot on the newly terraformed planet. (*Last Human* p. 169)

107 Professor Mamet. ('Psirens')

108 Dolochimps. (*Last Human* p. 109)

109 Because it ate all the other life forms' bodily effluence and reconstituted it into smokeless fuel. (*Last Human* p. 17)

110 By throwing himself on top of it. ('Psirens')

111 John Warburton, a bio-engineer. ('Beyond a Joke')

112 A mechanoid would never crack open a human's rib cage and use his right lung as a bedpan. (*Backwards* p. 196)

113 Three. ('Emohawk – Polymorph II')

114 Gary. ('Kryten')

115 While the crew were on the SSS *Esperanto*. ('Nanarchy')

116 Several hundred centuries. (*Backwards* p. 192)

117 Twelve. (*Infinity* p. 217)

118 Gordon's. ('Better Than Life')

119 Exploring Lister's laundry basket. ('Nanarchy')

120 His sanity chip. ('The Last Day')

121 Twenty-two. (*Better Than Life* p. 33)

122 Telepathy. (*Better Than Life* p. 174)

123 In his negadrive. ('Beyond a Joke')

Crossword 3
'Back to Reality'

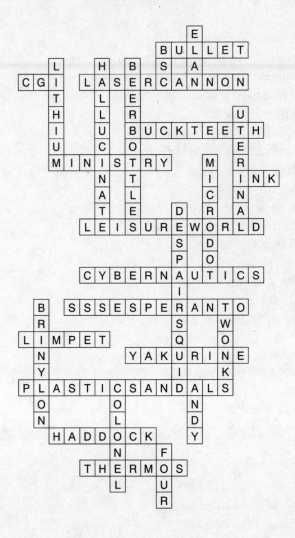

'Holly, I haven't the slightest clue what you're drivelling about!'

1 Lister. ('Backwards')
2 Kryten. ('Duct Soup')
3 Rimmer in Lister's body. ('Bodyswap')
4 Kryten. ('DNA')
5 Lister. ('Blue')
6 Rimmer. ('Balance of Power')
7 Lister. ('Tikka to Ride')
8 Holly. ('Kryten')
9 Kryten. ('Nanarchy')
10 Rimmer. ('Better Than Life')
11 Kryten. ('Beyond a Joke')
12 Rimmer. ('Back to Reality')
13 Holly. ('Confidence and Paranoia')
14 Kochanski. ('Epideme')
15 Rimmer. ('Camille')
16 Cat. ('Demons and Angels')
17 Padre. ('Dimension Jump')
18 Ace Rimmer. ('Stoke Me a Clipper')
19 Kryten. ('The Last Day')
20 Lister. ('Me²')
21 Cat. ('DNA')
22 Duane Dibbley. ('Emohawk – Polymorph II')
23 Holly. ('Nanarchy')
24 Lister. ('The End')
25 Lister. ('Beyond a Joke')
26 Lister. ('Future Echoes')
27 Lister. ('Backwards')

28 Lister. ('Bodyswap')

29 Kryten. ('Blue')

30 Lister. ('Future Echoes')

31 Jimmy. ('Gunmen of the Apocalypse')

32 Cat. ('Holoship')

33 Lister. ('The Inquisitor')

34 Cat. ('Duct Soup')

35 Psiren Kochanski. ('Psirens')

36 Kryten. ('Stoke Me a Clipper')

37 Cat. ('Ouroboros')

38 Rimmer. ('Justice')

39 J. F. Kennedy. ('Tikka to Ride')

40 Kryten. ('Kryten')

41 Lister. ('Thanks for the Memory')

42 Kryten. ('Nanarchy')

43 Rimmer. ('Better Than Life')

44 Lister. ('Epideme')

45 Cat. ('Back to Reality')

46 Rimmer. ('Quarantine')

47 Rimmer. ('Psirens')

48 Able. ('Beyond a Joke')

49 Rimmer. ('The Last Day')

50 Lister. ('Legion')

51 Ace Rimmer. ('Dimension Jump')

52 Lister. ('Blue')

53 Gilbert. ('Timeslides')

54 Rimmer. ('Waiting for God')

55 Lister. ('Duct Soup')

56 High Rimmer. ('Demons and Angels')

57 Duane Dibbley. ('Back to Reality')

58 Ace Rimmer. ('Dimension Jump')

59 Kryten. ('Ouroboros')
60 Paranoia. ('Confidence and Paranoia')
61 Rimmer. ('Marooned')
62 Cat. ('Blue')
63 Rimmer 2. ('Me^2')
64 Spare Head Two. ('Tikka to Ride')
65 Cat. ('Meltdown')
66 Lister. ('Waiting for God')
67 Kryten. ('Beyond a Joke')
68 Arlene Rimmer. ('Parallel Universe')
69 Epideme. ('Epideme')
70 Kryten. ('Polymorph')
71 Cat. ('Balance of Power')
72 Lister. ('Duct Soup')
73 Cat. ('Polymorph')
74 Lister. ('Psirens')
75 Lister. ('White Hole')
76 Cat. ('Beyond a Joke')
77 Cat and Kryten. ('Quarantine')
78 Rimmer. ('Marooned')
79 Cat. ('Epideme')
80 Holly. ('Me^2')
81 Cat. ('Nanarchy')
82 Holly. ('Queeg')
83 Rimmer's clone. ('Rimmerworld')
84 Ace Rimmer. ('Stoke Me a Clipper')
85 Rimmer. ('Stasis Leak')
86 Rimmer. ('Terrorform')
87 Lister. ('Beyond a Joke')
88 Cat. ('Thanks for the Memory')
89 Lister. ('Waiting for God')

90 Kryten. ('Nanarchy')
91 Rimmer 2. ('Me²')
92 Lister. ('Waiting for God')
93 Lister. ('White Hole')
94 Holly. ('Back to Reality')

'Purple alert!'

1 Red. ('The End')
2 Pink. ('Tikka to Ride')
3 Grey and white. ('Back to Reality')
4 Red. ('Waiting for God')
5 White. ('Stoke Me a Clipper')
6 Red. ('Polymorph')
7 Blue. ('Ouroboros')
8 Red. ('Balance of Power')
9 Grey with yellow, pink and black stripes. ('Waiting for God')
10 Yellow. ('Confidence and Paranoia')
11 Blue. ('Me²')
12 Yellow. ('Kryten')
13 Red with white polka dots. ('Quarantine')
14 Red. ('Duct Soup')
15 Green. ('Stasis Leak')
16 Green. ('The End')
17 Red. ('Better Than Life')
18 Red. ('The End')

19 Yellow. ('Back to Reality')
20 Black. ('Queeg')
21 Pink and orange(ish). ('Parallel Universe')
22 Pink. ('Marooned')
23 Brown. ('Back to Reality')
24 Blue and white. ('Thanks for the Memory')
25 Green bucket with a red handle, and a yellow spade.
    ('Polymorph')
26 Red. ('Timeslides')
27 Blue. ('The End')
28 Blue. ('The Last Day')
29 Red. ('Balance of Power')
30 Green. ('Dimension Jump')
31 Blue. ('Quarantine')
32 Yellow. ('Better Than Life')
33 Pink. ('Back to Reality')
34 Grey. ('Waiting for God')
35 Multicoloured stripes. ('Kryten')
36 Green with white spots. ('Back to Reality')
37 Silver. ('Confidence and Paranoia')
38 Black. ('Duct Soup')
39 Green. ('Balance of Power')
40 Green. ('Kryten')
41 Red. ('Out of Time')
42 Yellow. ('Thanks for the Memory')
43 Red. ('Timeslides')
44 Blue. ('The End')
45 Blue. ('Ouroboros')
46 Yellow. ('Balance of Power')
47 Red and black tartan. ('Better Than Life')
48 Red. ('Me²')

49 Yellow. ('Future Echoes')
50 Green. ('Beyond a Joke')
51 Red and white. ('Stoke Me a Clipper')
52 Yellow. ('Blue')

Word search 4
'Would you like some toast?'

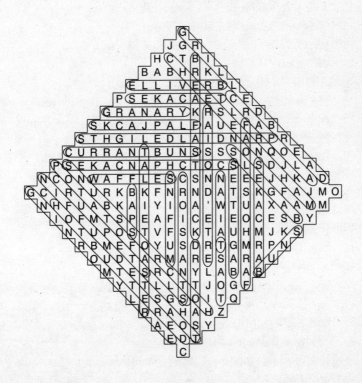

'Novelty condom head!'

1 Because Lister asked for brown ketchup with lobster. ('Beyond a Joke')

2 Invalidate his guarantee. ('Terrorform')

3 Being Arnold J. Rimmer. ('Justice')

4 His groinal box fell into Rimmer's soup. ('Stoke Me a Clipper')

5 2%. ('The Last Day')

6 The ship's trash file. ('Tikka to Ride')

7 Chloroform. ('Demons and Angels')

8 He's a fully qualified Bachelor of Sanitation. ('Epideme')

9 A Ronald Reagan mask. ('Backwards')

10 He stretches each 'container' over his head and irons it from there. ('Blue')

11 Proving Rimmer was a dork. ('Justice')

12 In the officers' club. ('The Last Day')

13 To roast a chicken in. ('Stoke Me a Clipper')

14 Rimmer. ('Polymorph')

15 4X2C. ('Beyond a Joke')

16 Rimmer. ('Justice')

17 The matter paddle. ('Demons and Angels')

18 A jamjar and a postcard. ('Nanarchy')

19 Mutiny. ('Camille')

20 At two o'clock in the morning. ('Epideme')

21 When he had thrown the triplicator into reverse. ('Demons and Angels')

22 In the research labs on Z deck. ('Meltdown')

23 At 'Rimmer's' funeral service. ('Stoke Me a Clipper')

24 Thirty thousand years. ('DNA')
25 Talkie Toaster. ('White Hole')
26 Behind his right ear. ('Tikka to Ride')
27 Rimmer. ('Justice')
28 Lavatorial Sciences. ('Epideme')
29 Kryten additional 001. ('The Inquisitor')
30 The big-eared ugly one. ('Stoke Me a Clipper')

'This isn't a meal, it's an autopsy!'

1 Clearhead alcohol-free vodka. (*Backwards* p. 82)
2 The cargo bay. ('Beyond a Joke')
3 Rimmer. ('Stasis Leak')
4 A swan in repose. (*Last Human* p. 58)
5 Supply deck B had been flooded when the laser cannon had breached the main water tank. ('Tikka to Ride')
6 The Palace of Versailles. (*Better Than Life* p. 3)
7 Sherry. ('Me²')
8 Five minutes. ('Polymorph')
9 Custard stains. ('Waiting for God')
10 Get a drink. (*Last Human* p. 133)
11 The ducks up on Potter's pond. (*Better Than Life* p. 9)
12 A stool bucket. ('Polymorph')
13 Try it out on his athlete's foot. ('Better Than Life')
14 Cinzano Bianco and advocaat. ('Tikka to Ride')
15 Gazpacho soup. ('Me²')
16 Off Regent Street in London. (*Infinity* p. 15)

17 His right index finger. ('Waiting for God')
18 Edam. ('Camille')
19 Two days. (*Infinity* p. 17)
20 Caviar Vindaloo, half rice, half chips and lots more bread and butter to follow. Plus Dom Perignon 1944 in a pint mug. ('Better Than Life')
21 A meeting place where people attempt to achieve advanced states of mental incompetence by the repeated consumption of fermented vegetable drinks. ('Timeslides')
22 An entire bottle of Cinzano Bianco, and a triple fried-egg sandwich with chilli sauce and chutney. (*Better Than Life* p. 217)
23 A raspberry pavlova in onion gravy. (*Infinity* p. 141)
24 Monday. ('Tikka to Ride')
25 Jam roly-poly. ('Out of Time')
26 A metal bucket. ('Future Echoes')
27 Grapes (stalks) and an orange (peel). ('Confidence and Paranoia')
28 Five days. ('Quarantine')
29 Lister. ('Duct Soup')
30 The black twisty ones that everybody hates. ('Legion')
31 Roast chicken, noisettes of pork and a joint of beef – all cooked; asparagus, stuffed olives, French bread, fresh strawberries; whipped cream, Belgian chocolates, a variety of cheeses and two bottles of chilled Marne Valley vintage champagne. (*Last Human* p. 83)
32 Kidney bowls. ('Polymorph')
33 All the nutty fruit snack bars. ('Blue')
34 Eighteen days ago, 11.36, Tuesday 3rd (two rounds). ('Waiting for God')

35 Mild, Hot, Very Hot, Book A Plot In The Cemetery Matie. (*Better Than Life* p. 32)

36 A double Jim Daniels bourbon. (*Last Human* p. 82)

37 By cutting out the fourth round of toast. ('Emohawk – Polymorph II')

38 Three poppadoms with mango chutney, little onions, dill pickle, day-glo green mint sauce, that weird red stuff, shami kebab starter, chicken vindaloo, kamikaze hot with a fire extinguisher on stand-by. Two scoops of koffi ice cream and two indigestion tablets. ('Tikka to Ride')

39 Prime fillet steak in blue cheese sauce, charcoal broiled in garlic butter. ('Marooned')

40 The servers in the Hot Dog and Doughnut Diner. ('Waiting for God')

41 Glen Fujiyama. (*Infinity* p. 39)

42 Because everyone was too polite to take it. ('Me²')

43 Kochanski. ('Ouroboros')

44 God (*Infinity* p. 281)

45 Buddha. (*Better Than Life* p. 39)

46 An artificial insemination syringe for cows. ('Polymorph')

47 Green wine. ('Beyond a Joke')

48 In the shape of an envelope. ('Thanks for the Memory')

49 Blue. (*Last Human* p. 172)

50 Curry sauce. ('Holoship')

51 Rimmer. ('Blue')

52 The 'lows'. ('Demons and Angels')

53 A piece of poppadom. (*Last Human* p. 298)

54 Five hundred. ('Tikka to Ride')

55 Green. ('Waiting for God')

56 Two weeks' PD. ('Stasis Leak')

57 At five o'clock. (*Infinity* p. 259)

58 Rotting meat flavour. ('Parallel Universe')

59 Cottage cheese with pineapple chunks. ('Duct Soup')

60 Dog's milk. ('Kryten', or *Infinity* p. 174)

61 A bagful of garlic cloves. (*Better Than Life* p. 66)

62 Lobster à la greque. ('Timeslides')

63 Because it makes your breath smell like a lift full of senile donkeys returning from a garlic-eating contest. ('Blue')

64 They bounced. ('Better Than Life')

65 Rimmer. (*Last Human* p. 268)

66 Waffles, dripping in honey and jam, with three fried eggs on the side, coated in cheese. ('Tikka to Ride')

67 Strut his funky stuff. ('The Last Day')

68 Three hours. ('Better Than Life')

69 Two days. ('Beyond a Joke')

70 In *Starbug*'s tool cupboard. ('Marooned')

71 Twenty-three. (*Better Than Life* p. 81)

72 A French loaf. ('Timeslides')

73 An olive. (*Better Than Life* p. 149)

74 Four, from the SS *Centauri*'s stasis block. ('Beyond a Joke')

75 About one hour. ('Demons and Angels')

76 Seventy-three. (*Better Than Life* p. 157)

77 Six. ('Balance of Power')

78 The Fat Bastarderia. ('Tikka to Ride')

79 Number one in quality, number one in taste. ('Bodyswap')

80 Table K on the second terrace. ('Better Than Life')

81 Six days. ('Marooned')

82 Because he couldn't wait to get the wrapper off and taste the salty goodness. ('Duct Soup')

83 Popcorn. ('Camille')

84 Playing squash with a bloke called Gerald. ('DNA')

85 A cappuccino coffee and a tuna and mayonnaise sandwich. (*Better Than Life* p. 222)

86 A chicken vindaloo. ('DNA')

87 Toastie toppers, cinema hot dogs and sweaty kebabs with stringy brown lettuce coming out. ('Demons and Angels')

88 Because no bugger'll drink it. ('Kryten', or *Infinity* p. 174)

89 French apples. ('Beyond a Joke')

90 They make him chuck. ('Quarantine')

91 Space weevils. ('Legion')

92 Cat. ('Gunmen of the Apocalypse')

93 Rabbit. (*Better Than Life* p. 117)

94 In the fridge. ('Blue')

95 When the polymorph sucked out his vanity. (*Better Than Life* p. 202)

96 Lister. ('Gunmen of the Apocalypse')

97 Lister and Cashier Number Four. ('Duct Soup')

98 Rimmer's future self. ('Out of Time')

99 In his hat. ('The Last Day')

100 Lister. ('Beyond a Joke')

101 A glass of sterilized milk. ('Timeslides')

102 Like he's a pot of cottage cheese with pineapple chunks in. ('Duct Soup')

Staircase 4

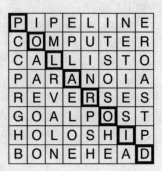

P	I	P	E	L	I	N	E

'Well, forget it, Lister. Not if you were the last man alive'

1 Rimmer's mum. Rimmer. ('Dimension Jump')
2 Captain Voorhese. Lister. ('Stoke Me a Clipper')
3 Cat. Cat. ('Timeslides')
4 Holly. Cat. ('DNA')
5 Frank. Lister. ('Ouroboros')
6 Rimmer. Lister. ('Balance of Power')
7 Captain Hollister. Rimmer. ('Stasis Leak')
8 Lister. Cat. ('Demons and Angels')
9 Rimmer. Rimmer. ('Out of Time')
10 Lister. Holly. ('Queeg')
11 Lister. Cat. ('Backwards')
12 Film character. Rimmer. ('Holoship')
13 Rimmer. Rimmer. ('Waiting for God')

14 Rimmer. Kryten. ('Legion')

15 Warning announcement. Cat. ('Polymorph')

16 Kryten. Kryten. ('Blue')

17 Kryten. Lister. ('Rimmerworld')

18 Kryten. Cat. ('Justice')

19 Rimmer. Lister. ('Meltdown')

20 Cat. Kryten. ('Epideme')

21 Kryten, Kryten. ('Back to Reality')

22 Lister. Kochanski. ('Duck Soup')

23 Rimmer. Rimmer. ('Bodyswap')

24 Lister. Lister. ('Me²')

25 The Inquisitor. Lister. ('The Inquisitor')

26 Holly. Lister. ('Thanks for the Memory')

27 Lister. Kryten. ('Beyond a Joke')

28 Carol. Rimmer 2. ('Confidence and Paranoia')

29 Kryten. Kryten. ('White Hole')

30 Kryten's CPU. Lister, Cat and Kryten. ('Terrorform')

31 Lister. Lister. ('Psirens')

32 Lister. Lister. ('Camille')

33 Lister. Lister. ('The End')

34 Holly. Rimmer. ('Marooned')

35 Rimmer. Duane Dibbley. ('Emohawk – Polymorph II')

36 Kryten. Lister. ('Quarantine')

37 Lister. Taxman. ('Better Than Life')

38 Kryten. Kryten. ('The Last Day')

39 Lister. Lister. ('Tikka to Ride')

40 Lister. Lister. ('Future Echoes')

41 Philip (Lister). The crew. ('Gunmen of the Apocalypse')

42 Kryten. Cat. ('Nanarchy')

43 Cat. Rimmer. ('Parallel Universe')

44 Kelly. Kryten. ('Kryten')

Crossword 4
'Dimension Jump'

'Shakespeare? Who's Shakespeare?'

1 Rimmer. (*Backwards* p. 161)
2 Rimmer. (*Better Than Life* p. 219)
3 Holly. (*Backwards* p. 189)
4 Rimmer's duplicate. (*Infinity* p. 236)
5 Kryten. (*Backwards* p. 212)
6 Cat. (*Better Than Life* p. 19)
7 Kinitawowi chief. (*Last Human* p. 96)
8 Rimmer. (*Backwards* p. 154)
9 Rimmer. (*Infinity* p. 143)
10 Lister. (*Backwards* p. 323)
11 Tonto Jitterman. (*Better Than Life* p. 58)
12 Rimmer. (*Backwards* p. 91)
13 Lister's inner voice. (*Last Human* p. 7)
14 Bob the Sergeant on Europa. (*Backwards* p. 122)
15 Talkie Toaster. (*Better Than Life* p. 183)
16 Lister. (*Backwards* p. 49)
17 Ace Rimmer. (*Backwards* p. 220)
18 Rimmer. (*Infinity* p. 23)
19 Rimmer. (*Backwards* p. 185)
20 John F. Kennedy. (*Better Than Life* p. 3)
21 Lister. (*Backwards* p. 298)
22 Rimmer. (*Backwards* p. 37)
23 Kryten. (*Backwards* p. 203)
24 Cat. (*Backwards* p. 333)
25 Rimmer. (*Better Than Life* p. 41)
26 Rimmer. (*Backwards* p. 156)
27 Lister's *doppelgänger*. (*Last Human* p. 130)

28 Cat. (*Backwards* p. 135)
29 Lister. (*Better Than Life* p. 193)
30 Rimmer. (*Infinity* p. 220)
31 Talkie Toaster. (*Better Than Life* p. 157)
32 Kryten. (*Last Human* p. 205)
33 God. (*Infinity* p. 281)
34 Rimmer. (*Backwards* p. 23)
35 Cat. (*Backwards* p. 265)
36 Cat. (*Last Human* p. 216)
37 Cat. (*Backwards* p. 317)
38 Cat. (*Last Human* p. 248)
39 Frank Saunders. (*Infinity* p. 27)
40 Rimmer. (*Backwards* p. 47)
41 Rimmer. (*Infinity* p. 52)
42 Lister. (*Last Human* p. 308)
43 Rimmer. (*Backwards* p. 305)
44 Rimmer. (*Last Human* p. 96)
45 Lister. (*Infinity* p. 180)
46 Weiner. (*Infinity* p. 29)

'There's an old human saying – If you're going to talk garbage, expect pain'

1 Cat. ('Backwards')
2 *Centauri* simulant. ('Beyond a Joke')
3 Rimmer. ('Dimension Jump')
4 Rimmer. ('Thanks for the Memory')
5 Cat. ('Nanarchy')

6 Lister. ('Future Echoes')

7 Talkie Toaster. ('White Hole')

8 A German soldier. ('Stoke Me a Clipper')

9 Holly. ('Bodyswap')

10 Cat. ('Balance of Power')

11 Lister. ('Better Than Life')

12 Jake Bullet. ('Back to Reality')

13 Holly. ('Camille')

14 Epideme. ('Epideme')

15 High Rimmer. ('Demons and Angels')

16 Spare Head Two. ('Tikka to Ride')

17 Ace Rimmer. ('Dimension Jump')

18 Holly. ('Confidence and Paranoia')

19 Cat. ('Beyond a Joke')

20 Kryten. ('DNA')

21 Cat. ('The End')

22 Lister. ('Blue')

23 Talkie Toaster. ('Future Echoes')

24 Cat. ('Duct Soup')

25 Ms Harrison. ('Holoship')

26 Cat. ('Justice')

27 Andy. ('Back to Reality')

28 Able. ('Beyond a Joke')

29 Lister. ('Me²')

30 Lister. ('Duct Soup')

31 Confidence. ('Confidence and Paranoia')

32 Lister. ('Epideme')

33 Cat Inquisitor. ('The Inquisitor')

34 Cat. ('White Hole')

35 Holly. ('Kryten')

36 Lister. ('Ouroboros')

37 Cat. ('Me²')
38 Kryten. ('Blue')
39 Lister. ('Waiting for God')
40 Kochanski. ('Nanarchy')
41 Rimmer as Kochanski's hologram. ('Balance of Power')
42 Rimmer. ('Kryten')
43 Cat. ('Psirens')
44 Kryten. ('Quarantine')
45 Rimmer. ('Better Than Life')
46 Lister. ('Epideme')
47 Rimmer. ('Dimension Jump')
48 Cat. ('Waiting for God')
49 Able. ('Beyond a Joke')
50 Rimmer. ('Marooned')
51 Hudzen. ('The Last Day')
52 Kryten. ('Legion')
53 Rimmer. ('Tikka to Ride')
54 Carole Brown in Lister's body. ('Bodyswap')
55 Holly. ('Nanarchy')
56 Chen. ('Balance of Power')
57 Cat. ('Blue')
58 Rimmer 2. ('Me²')
59 Holly. ('Future Echoes')
60 Kochanski. ('Ouroboros')
61 Caligula. ('Meltdown')
62 Lister. ('Stoke Me a Clipper')
63 Rimmer. ('Waiting for God')
64 Holly. ('Parallel Universe')
65 Lister. ('Nanarchy')
66 Kryten. ('Polymorph')
67 Rimmer. ('Kryten')

68 Kryten. ('Out of Time')
69 Kochanski. ('Duct Soup')
70 Lister. ('Demons and Angels')
71 Kryten. ('Psirens')
72 Cat. ('Epideme')
73 Rimmer. ('Quarantine')
74 Rimmer. ('Blue')
75 Cat. ('The Inquisitor')
76 Lister. ('Tikka to Ride')
77 Lister. ('Queeg')
78 Holly. ('Back to Reality')
79 Cat. ('Nanarchy')
80 Rimmer. ('Stasis Leak')
81 Rimmer. ('Terrorform')
82 Kryten. ('Duct Soup')
83 Holly. ('Thanks for the Memory')
84 Rimmer. ('Waiting for God')
85 Lister. ('Timeslides')
86 Kryten. ('Ouroboros')
87 Talkie Toaster. ('White Hole')
88 Arlene Rimmer. ('Parallel Universe')
89 Lister. ('Blue')
90 Lister. ('Psirens')
91 Rimmer. ('Terrorform')
92 Cat. ('Thanks for the Memory')
93 Gilbert. ('Timeslides')
94 Cat. ('Duct Soup')

Word search 5
Episodes

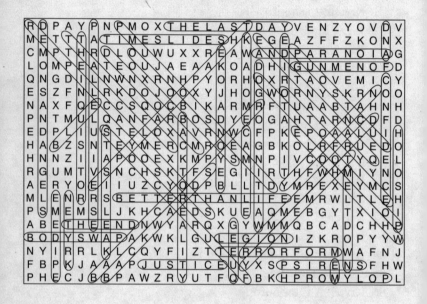

'Goalpost head!'

1 Explaining to Captain Hollister why he had not sealed the drive plate properly. ('The End')

2 He's a small-minded, bureaucratic, incompetent, cowardly little person. ('Stoke Me a Clipper')

3 Runner-up in the Second World War. ('Timeslides')

4 One up, one down and one to polish. ('Blue')

5 A frozen husky. ('White Hole')

6 Unknown. ('Holoship')

7 Army boots. ('Quarantine')

8 We don't use our tongues to clean our own genitals. ('Confidence and Paranoia')

9 So they each spent the same amount of time in his shoes. ('Blue')

10 Lister. ('Psirens')

11 Andy. ('Back to Reality')

12 Rachel. ('Stoke Me a Clipper')

13 Stuck his pencil up Captain Hollister's nose and ripped up and ate his wife's photograph. ('Stasis Leak')

14 A eunuch. ('Stoke Me a Clipper')

15 Popeye the Sailor Man. ('DNA')

16 Argon 5. ('Blue')

17 2.30 in the morning. ('Meltdown')

18 She was a model. ('Camille')

19 Twenty-four to twenty-five. ('Bodyswap')

20 Fifteen. ('Marooned')

21 The definitive history of pockets. ('Stoke Me a Clipper')

22 'All You Need Is Love'. ('Polymorph')

23 Fifteen. ('Queeg')

24 He sometimes went out of the room. ('Blue')

25 Underneath the scanner table. ('Legion')

26 Spanish television. ('Thanks for the Memory')

27 Because a book has got a spine. ('Stoke Me a Clipper')

28 Porky Roebuck. ('Marooned')

29 Set fire to them. ('Stoke Me a Clipper')

30 Two senior officers. ('Stasis Leak')

31 He cowers under tables with a colander on his head. ('Stoke Me a Clipper')

Word search 6
The Rimmer Experience

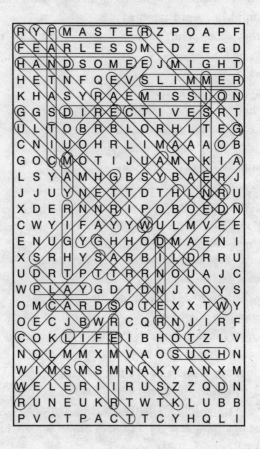

'It took me ages to mark these cards!'

1 Italian Driver. (*Infinity* p. 135)
2 *Casablanca*. ('Camille')
3 Julius Caesar. (*Better Than Life* p. 3)
4 Three weeks. ('Dimension Jump')
5 Red. ('Waiting for God')
6 The one-armed bandit. ('Nanarchy')
7 Four years. ('Back to Reality')
8 A large packet of extra-spicy tortilla chips and a really good horror movie. ('Epideme')
9 Seventeen games, three and a half hours. (*Infinity* p. 151)
10 One wellington boot and a box of a hundred assorted tampons that glow in the dark. ('Blue')
11 The cha-cha. ('Confidence and Paranoia')
12 In the canal. ('Dimension Jump')
13 Two thousand. (*Last Human* p. 54)
14 To get Kochanski. ('Back to Reality')
15 Gordon. ('Better Than Life')
16 *Chitty-Chitty Bang-Bang*. (*Last Human* p. 166)
17 The Last Supper. (*Better Than Life* p. 4)
18 Three. ('Blue')
19 A Czechoslovakian documentary about 15th-century cloud formations. (*Last Human* p. 166)
20 Camille and himself. ('Camille')
21 Belgium. ('Dimension Jump')
22 Channel 72. ('Beyond a Joke')
23 Kochanski. (*Last Human* p. 255)
24 Zeke. (*Backwards* p. 147)

25 A novel by Victor Hugo. ('Waiting for God')

26 Eight. (*Backwards* p. 167)

27 The tuba. (*Better Than Life* p. 11)

28 Since he was sixteen. ('Marooned')

29 Kochanski. (*Last Human* p. 38)

30 A little over forty-seven years. (*Backwards* p. 174)

31 The WW2 game. ('Beyond a Joke')

32 Bobby Darroch. (*Backwards* p. 342)

33 A crossword book. ('Future Echoes')

34 Because there were no fish. ('Dimension Jump')

35 Saturday. ('Balance of Power')

36 Twice. ('Blue')

37 'The Indling Song'. ('Confidence and Paranoia')

38 By recreating key events in his life from his diaries. ('Blue')

39 For three-year-olds. ('Waiting for God')

40 Howard's. (*Backwards* p. 167)

41 Into orbit. ('Blue')

42 Five. ('Me²')

43 Wilma Shakespeare. ('Parallel Universe')

44 'Morning Has Broken'. (*Better Than Life* p. 31)

45 *Androids*. ('Kryten')

46 'God Rest Ye Merry, Gentlemen'. (*Infinity* p. 259)

47 Chess pawns. ('Better Than Life')

48 Nine-hole. ('Blue')

49 Lister. (*Backwards* p. 163)

50 Two specially bred Venusian fighting snails. (*Infinity* p. 54)

51 Four. ('Better Than Life')

52 To go up to the laundry room and fold some sheets. ('The Last Day')

53 Dicky Duckworth. (*Backwards* p. 170)

54 Three. ('Marooned')

55 Seven hundred and ninety-three. (*Better Than Life* p. 35)

56 A pair of tights. ('Timeslides')

57 The last two weeks in July and the weekend before Christmas. ('Bodyswap')

58 Jazz FM. ('DNA')

59 They failed to qualify for the second round. (*Better Than Life* p. 172)

60 Zach Rattler. (*Backwards* p. 173)

61 Twenty. ('Back to Reality')

62 *Baked Bean Bombshells*, Volume 12. ('Blue')

63 *Jaws*. ('Dimension Jump')

64 Kochanski. ('Ouroboros')

65 Being in his own garden, planting it and making it grow. ('Kryten')

66 Danger – Government Health Warning. This music can make you irritable and irrational and has been linked with disorders of the nervous system and bowels. ('Balance of Power')

67 Playing solo squash. (*Infinity* p. 163)

68 The long, drawn-out death-rattle of a man suffering from terminal flatulence. ('Dimension Jump')

69 That his brothers were behind him threatening to peg him to the ground, smear his body with bilberry jam and leave him to be eaten alive by armies of soldier ants. (*Backwards* p. 168)

70 So he could be the dice. ('Psirens')

71 Locker number 68. A gold necklace, a bundle of cash and a nude wrestling video. ('Blue')

72 In the recreation room. (*Infinity* p. 135)
73 He allowed himself to read only 0.819178 words a day.
   (*Backwards* p. 174)

Crossword 5
'Tikka to Ride'

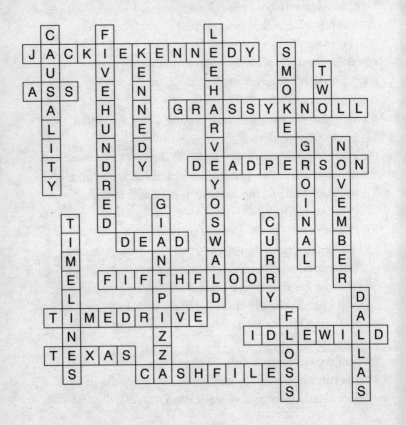

'Excuse me, Voter Colonel – but is this some kind of test?'

1 Everything. ('Out of Time')
2 Lister's. ('Beyond a Joke')
3 Uncle Arnie fries them alive with his hex vision. ('Quarantine')
4 To pee or not to pee. ('Duct Soup')
5 Queeg. ('Queeg')
6 Beryl. ('Stoke Me a Clipper')
7 Dorksville. ('Demons and Angels')
8 Friday. ('Tikka to Ride')
9 Modems or speaking slide-rules. ('The End')
10 It's nature's way of telling you to buy a flat cap and a pair of driving gloves. ('Ouroboros')
11 In the shower. ('Meltdown')
12 Esperanto and quantum theory. ('Me^2')
13 Rimmer. ('Balance of Power')
14 Victor Laszlo. ('Camille')
15 HOL-MEM, PASSWORD, OVERWRITE, THE NOVELS OF CHRISTIE, AGATHA, then press 'erase'. ('Confidence and Paranoia')
16 1778. ('Epideme')
17 Commit any act of injustice. ('Justice')
18 In the *Electronic Bible*. ('The Last Day')
19 212%. ('Tikka to Ride')
20 Decontaminate the officers' block. ('Confidence and Paranoia')
21 In the microdot in the 'i' of Rimmer's swimming certificate. ('Back to Reality')
22 Because he's a gutless, spineless, gormless, directionless,

neurotic, under-achieving, snivelling, cowardly pile of smeg. ('Stoke Me a Clipper')

23 Middle of the night, take them out into a blizzard, remove their pyjamas and just leave them to it. ('White Hole')

24 Barbara Bellini. ('Justice')

25 Him being Alexander the Great's chief eunuch. ('Marooned')

26 Kochanski's. ('Duct Soup')

27 Handcuffs, a banana and crisp sandwich, his diary and a brown-paper parcel. ('Timeslides')

28 Cuba. ('Tikka to Ride')

29 Rimmer. ('Demons and Angels')

30 Confidence and Paranoia. ('Confidence and Paranoia')

31 In the 19th century. ('Beyond a Joke')

32 Pope Gregory and Elvis Presley. ('Meltdown')

33 Rimmer was going to snap his guitar in half. ('The End')

34 Kryten. ('Nanarchy')

35 Holoship. ('Holoship')

36 Three weeks. ('Backwards')

37 Supply pipe 28. ('Waiting for God')

38 Lister of Smeg. ('Stoke Me a Clipper')

39 £15. ('Marooned')

40 Second-rate scum. ('Ouroboros')

41 From the excitement. ('Kryten')

42 Three. ('Tikka to Ride')

43 Eastbourne. ('White Hole')

44 Next door. ('Me²')

45 Rimmer. ('Dimension Jump')

46 A keyring with a 'C' on it. ('Duct Soup')

47 Two thousand. ('White Hole')

48 Tarka Dhal. ('Gunmen of the Apocalypse')

49 Napoleon. ('Me²')

50 Three. ('Beyond a Joke')

51 Rimmer. ('Rimmerworld')

52 The Hammond Organ Owners' Society. ('Dimension Jump')

53 Finding Kryten's nanobots. ('Nanarchy')

54 Because there were no sheep on board. ('Waiting for God')

55 £17.50. ('Me²')

56 Navigation Officer. ('Holoship')

57 Thicky Holden. ('Timeslides')

58 J. Edgar Hoover. ('Tikka to Ride')

59 A cassette for recording your last will and testament. ('Stasis Leak')

60 Swindon. ('Epideme')

61 The DNA modifier. ('DNA')

62 Eighteen weeks. ('Waiting for God')

63 A shelf. ('Kryten', or *Infinity* p. 179)

64 Fish bait. ('Demons and Angels')

65 To move out of the quarters he shared with Lister. ('Me²')

66 'Ace-hole'. ('Kryten', or *Infinity* p. 179)

67 Twelve hours. ('Tikka to Ride')

68 Act V, Henry VIII. ('Marooned')

69 H'idiot. ('Confidence and Paranoia')

70 To the Taj Mahal Tandoori Restaurant behind the JMC building in London (back table, quiet). ('Tikka to Ride')

71 On coat-hangers. ('Waiting for God', or *Infinity* p. 46)

72 Serving. ('Kryten')

73 Thursday. ('Thanks for the Memory')

74 Everlasting. ('Ouroboros')

75 Alison. ('Better Than Life')

76 Snappy. ('Stoke Me a Clipper')

77 From being live people to dead people. ('Back to Reality')

78 Ten years. ('Quarantine')

79 Kochanski. ('Blue')

80 He stood on his toe maliciously and with intent to wound. ('The End')

81 Six days and nights. ('Rimmerworld')

82 To allow them to examine the calibration on their time drive's mass compactor. ('Out of Time')

83 A tarantula crawling up his trousers. ('Better Than Life')

84 The fifth. ('Tikka to Ride')

85 A Javenese camphor-wood chest. ('Marooned')

86 Lister. ('Confidence and Paranoia')

87 Hué. ('Beyond a Joke')

88 Space Corps test ships. ('Out of Time')

89 Locker 58. ('Blue')

90 Successville. ('Me²')

91 Gazza. ('Timeslides')

92 Seven. ('Dimension Jump')

93 He was originally a soft-light hologram. ('Ouroboros')

94 It would have wiped out the Universe. ('The Inquisitor')

95 The bottom one. ('Me²')

96 Keeps you wet and smelly for up to 24 hours. ('Backwards')

97 Rimmer's mum's. ('Terrorform')

98 North Western Electricity Board. ('Me²')
99 Kochanski. ('Blue')
100 To have it ground down to line his drive.
    ('Timeslides')
101 Flight Co-ordinator McQueen. ('Holoship')
102 Caroline Carmen. ('Epideme')
103 Arrest them for being hallucinations. ('Confidence and
    Paranoia')
104 Four and three-quarters. ('Balance of Power')
105 The Hoover Open Prison, New York. ('Tikka to
    Ride')

Word search 7
Bedford Falls

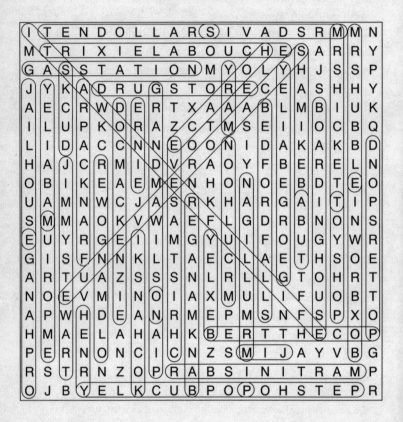

'Have you ever actually read any of it?'

1 Eighteen. (*Last Human* p. 85)
2 A box jacket in shimmering silver satin, with razor-thin lapels, and black vinyl trousers that taper into boots with winkle-picker toes. (*Backwards* p. 197)
3 Six. (*Infinity* p. 158)
4 'Lister, are you OK?' (*Backwards* p. 234)
5 A thousand metres deep and over five thousand metres wide. (*Last Human* p. 15)
6 George III and Brian Kidd (*Omnibus* p. 227). The fifth-century Norwegian warrior King Havac the Imbecile and his more idiotic half-brother (*Infinity* p. 227).
7 The one that said 'Legend of Rock'. (*Last Human* p. 10)
8 That you are not just any old durnoid, but you are *the* durniest of all the durnoids who ever dared to durn. (*Backwards* p. 6)
9 Through diligent hoovering. (*Better Than Life* p. 154)
10 A lethal weapon. (*Last Human* p. 256)
11 Japan. (*Better Than Life* p. 131)
12 Lister and Kryten. (*Last Human* p. 56)
13 Ace Rimmer. (*Backwards* p. 211)
14 Through the guard's walkie talkie, as radio waves. (*Better Than Life* p. 56)
15 A little under three weeks. (*Backwards* p. 162)
16 At Kilauea (a volcano) on Hawaii. (*Last Human* p. 159)
17 Three dollars. (*Infinity* p. 270)
18 Two K's. (*Better Than Life* p. 165)
19 In the cargo bays. (*Last Human* p. 46)

20 Wildfire's technical co-ordinator. (*Backwards* p. 103)

21 Ice. (*Backwards* p. 318)

22 Five. (*Last Human* p. 83)

23 Rimmer. (*Infinity* p. 244)

24 Mount Everest. (*Better Than Life* p. 167)

25 Two. (*Better Than Life* p. 222)

26 Within thirty-six hours. (*Last Human* p. 228)

27 Two and a half. (*Backwards* p. 179)

28 Seven. (*Infinity* p. 219)

29 Flowers. (*Better Than Life* p. 55)

30 Because it was a characteristic totally absent from his own programming. (*Last Human* p. 75)

31 Michael McGruder. (*Last Human* p. 156)

32 Holly. (*Backwards* p. 142)

33 For taking a three-cent trolley ride, having paid only a two-cent fare. (*Better Than Life* p. 8)

34 Purple. (*Last Human* p. 308)

35 Kirsty Fantozi. (*Infinity* p. 161)

36 Five thousand. (*Better Than Life* p. 39)

37 Thirty-sixth out of thirty-seven. (*Backwards* p. 5)

38 Rimmer's micro-minded mentality. (*Last Human* p. 298)

39 War Apocalypse. (*Backwards* p. 300)

40 Noon. (*Backwards* p. 13)

41 For hijacking rich people's bodies and taking them on joyrides. (*Better Than Life* p. 52)

42 Five. (*Last Human* p. 79)

43 He had destroyed the entire asteroid of Cyrius 3, looted and plundered his way across the entire belt, and destroyed a Starhopper which served Ariel 2, and was responsible for many deaths including that of the Regulator. (*Last Human* p. 77)

44 It was ransacked from a derelict. (*Last Human* p. 42)

45 Eight. (*Infinity* p. 176)

46 Rotting foodstuff. (*Better Than Life* p. 131)

47 South. (*Backwards* p. 52)

48 That the specific nature of the complaint does not contravene terrestrial laws, or colonial laws where such an offence is not deemed to have been committed within the boundaries of the aforementioned 'zero space' lanes as defined in section A92, para 17(d) . . . (Backwards p.176)

Well, that's what you get when you leave a solar-class mining vessel in the hands of a senile computer who could be outwitted by a losing contestant from Junior Criss Cross Quiz. (*Backwards* p. 176)

49 A small duvet. (*Better Than Life* p. 15)

50 Because he's dead. (*Last Human* p. 41)

51 Seven minutes. (*Backwards* p. 332)

52 Four. (*Last Human* p. 86)

53 $£50 billion. (*Infinity* p. 277)

54 Close to four hundred miles an hour. (*Last Human* p. 232)

55 About three hundred thousand. (*Better Than Life* p. 51)

56 Frank Rimmer's. (*Better Than Life* p. 27)

57 He changed 36/37 to 36/87 with a yellow crayon. (*Backwards* p. 5)

58 Red. (*Last Human* p. 83)

59 A bag of uncut Baquaii diamonds, a box of cheap cigars, an old rad pistol, a handful of plastic bottles containing info pills, and Kryten's right arm. (*Last Human* p. 141)

60 Under his hat. (*Infinity* p. 89)

61 Into the septic tank behind the sports ground. (*Better Than Life* p. 114)

62 By using the DNA of innocent penal colony internees. (*Last Human* p. 230)

63 Junior B. (*Backwards* p. 167)

64 Fifteen minutes. (*Infinity* p. 19)

65 Cat. (*Backwards* p. 227)

66 An inflatable dolphin with battery-operated fins. (*Better Than Life* p. 15)

67 Two years. (*Infinity* p. 297)

68 About half a teaspoonful. (*Last Human* p. 69)

69 Henry. (*Better Than Life* p. 9)

70 Lister. (*Better Than Life* p. 31)

71 Yellow and black stripes. (*Backwards* p. 169)

72 Six. (*Last Human* p. 194)

73 Fourteen. (*Better Than Life* p. 81)

74 Lister. (*Backwards* p. 119)

75 A decomposing body. (*Last Human* p. 275)

76 Kryten. (*Backwards* p. 65)

77 $5. (*Better Than Life* p. 8)

78 Since he was seventeen – eight years. (*Last Human* p. 18)

79 Kevin. (*Backwards* p. 84)

80 So they could never be mistaken for living people. (*Infinity* p. 27)

81 Old car radiators and exhaust pipes. (*Better Than Life* p. 166)

82 A million. (*Infinity* p. 267)

83 Five hours. (*Backwards* p. 19)

84 In the grain store. (*Backwards* p. 63)

85 Day-glo Deely-boppers, battery-propelled revolving bow-ties and yellow fishing waders. (*Better Than Life* p. 217)

86 Lister. (*Infinity* p. 110)

87 Winning may not be everything; but losing is nothing. (*Backwards* p. 170)

88 Help create a giant, fast-growing super-wheat. (*Last Human* p. 210)

89 John Milhous Nixon. (*Last Human* p. 153)

90 In the ice compartment of the fridge. (*Better Than Life* p. 79)

91 Kochanski. (*Last Human* p. 38)

92 1990. (*Better Than Life* p. iv)

93 Dr Alice Kellerman. (*Last Human* p. 193)

94 Scarcely four inches. (*Better Than Life* p. 109)

95 Purple. (*Infinity* p. 210)

96 Mary. (*Better Than Life* p. 10)

97 Floor 140. (*Infinity* p. 264)

98 Yvonne McGruder. (*Last Human* p. 212)

99 $£10 a day. (*Last Human* p. 166)

100 Four.

101 (1) Game Over; (2) She Rides; (3) Garbage World; (4) The End, and after.

102 Because he had it on backwards. (*Last Human* p. 288)

103 They recharge instead of discharging, and overload. (*Backwards* p. 20)

104 They had lost their individual personalities and become part of a Gestalt intelligence. (*Last Human* p. 168)

105 Einstein. (*Infinity* p. 73)

106 Old Ma Bailey. (*Better Than Life* p. 9)

107 They wanted an end to the Mystic system of justice. (*Last Human* p. 79)

108 A pair of zero-gee football shorts and a can of lager. (*Last Human* p. 11)

109 Sergeant. (*Backwards* p. 122)

110 Eight months. (*Better Than Life* p. 20)

111 He was a jerky clerk in an office. (*Last Human* p. 146)

112 They would have their shower units removed. (*Infinity* p. 128)

113 In his database in a muffle program. (*Last Human* p. 304)

114 Half past one. (*Backwards* p. 52)

115 Lister. (*Last Human* p. 298)

Crossword 6
'Marooned'

'He's making it up, isn't he? The bloody book doesn't exist'

1 Lister. (*Backwards* p. 333)

2 Lister. (*Better Than Life* p. 77)

3 Rimmer. (*Backwards* p. 197)

4 Mr Capote. (*Last Human* p. 84)

5 Bexley. (*Infinity* p. 270)

6 Lister's *doppelgänger*. (*Last Human* p. 135)

7 Lister. (*Better Than Life* p. 184)

8 Rimmer. (*Backwards* p. 306)

9 Kryten. (*Last Human* p. 241)

10 Juanita. (*Better Than Life* p. 42)

11 Rimmer. (*Backwards* p. 28)

12 Rimmer. (*Better Than Life* p. 141)

13 Cat. (*Backwards* p. 295)

14 Rimmer. (*Last Human* p. 214)

15 Juanita Chicata. (*Infinity* p. 268)

16 Rimmer. (*Backwards* p. 302)

17 Rimmer's body-tailor. (*Better Than Life* p. 13)

18 Rimmer. (*Backwards* p. 162)

19 Kryten. (*Better Than Life* p. 98)

20 Rimmer. (*Backwards* p. 185)

21 Rimmer. (*Last Human* p. 252)

22 Horace the bank manager. (*Infinity* p. 260)

23 Pestilence. (*Backwards* p. 307)

24 Cat. (*Better Than Life* p. 202)

25 Lister. (*Last Human* p. 220)

26 Will Carton. (*Backwards* p. 297)

27 Avril Dupont. (*Better Than Life* p. 131)

The Answers

28 Ace Rimmer. (*Backwards* p. 213)

29 Cat. (*Backwards* p. 156)

30 Holly. (*Infinity* p. 223)

31 Sheriff Will Carton. (*Backwards* p. 253)

32 Cat. (*Backwards* p. 320)

33 Rimmer. (*Backwards* p. 189)

34 Kryten. (*Last Human* p. 304)

35 Hologram in the Games Room on the *Nova 5*. (*Infinity* p. 198)

36 Petersen. (*Backwards* p. 124)

37 Cat. (*Last Human* p. 260)

38 Rimmer. (*Backwards* p. 42)

39 Android brothel madame. (*Infinity* p. 23)

40 Kryten. (*Backwards* p. 137)

41 Kryten. (*Backwards* p. 153)

42 Cat. (*Backwards* p. 197)

43 Lister's *doppelgänger*. (*Last Human* p. 287)

44 Mamie Pherson. (*Backwards* p. 83)

'I've come to regard you as . . . people . . . I've met'

1 His briefcase. ('Timeslides')

2 A canister from *Red Dwarf*. (*Backwards* p. 45)

3 The centrefold of this month's *Playzombie*. ('Epideme')

4 In the refectory. ('The End')

5 Porky Roebuck's. ('Queeg')

6 Little guy, bad toupee, used to work in catering. ('Duct Soup')

7 Pestilence. (*Backwards* p. 304)

8 Two dollars and twenty-five cents (he only accepted one dollar twenty-five). (*Better Than Life* p. 9)

9 Billy Belief. (*Backwards* p. 255)

10 His right arm. ('Balance of Power')

11 Hanger 101. (*Backwards* p. 89)

12 Because his head was shaped like a bullet. (*Better Than Life* p. 54)

13 Deb Lister. ('Parallel Universe')

14 Because he wasn't allowed alcohol. (*Backwards* p. 118)

15 His father. ('Better Than Life')

16 Arnold J. Rimmer. (*Last Human* p. 161)

17 Jimmy's. ('Gunmen of the Apocalypse')

18 Churchills. (*Backwards* p. 125)

19 French. (*Better Than Life* p. 64)

20 The refreshment tent. (*Backwards* p. 170)

21 Because he was too ugly. ('Balance of Power')

22 Because he wanted to play the field. ('Thanks for the Memory')

23 Two nickels. (*Backwards* p. 255)

24 An antique Smith & Wesson. (*Infinity* p. 26)

25 Straight after Gettysburg. (*Backwards* p. 293)

26 In the bath. (*Last Human* p. 213)

27 It had no hands on it. (*Backwards* p. 298)

28 Behind the perfume counter at Lewis's. ('Marooned')

29 In the shower. ('Epideme')

30 Shore Patrolwoman Henderson. (*Infinity* p. 36)

31 Fifty-seven. (*Backwards* p. 254)

32 Fred. ('Timeslides')

33 His right forefinger. (*Backwards* p. 313)

34 Tim. ('Ouroboros')

35 He flipped a red pool ball into his mouth. (*Backwards* p. 286)

36 Famine. (*Backwards* p. 312)

37 Pluto. ('Parallel Universe')

38 Grey. (*Backwards* p. 321)

39 An Encyclo implant chip. (*Last Human* p. 43)

40 Anorak, white socks, nylon shirt, plastic sandals, Airtex vest, cardigan, key to the Salvation Army hostel, Thermos and a toothbrush. ('Back to Reality')

41 'Bonehead'. (*Backwards* p. 170)

42 Tom and Beth Thornton. (*Last Human* p. 145)

43 Five years. (*Infinity* p. 18)

44 Six feet two. (*Last Human* p. 182)

45 Melissa. (*Backwards* p. 126)

46 Midnight. ('Marooned')

47 Almost nine. (*Backwards* p. 169)

48 Southport. ('Thanks for the Memory')

49 Luigi. ('Timeslides')

50 Esther. (*Backwards* p. 252)

51 Miranda. (*Last Human* p. 268)

52 Karen. ('Epideme')

53 George McIntyre. ('The End')

54 Ben. (*Last Human* p. 277)

55 Pick his nose with his thumb. (*Backwards* p. 231)

56 Bullet-head Heinman. (*Backwards* p. 169)

57 Fourteen years. ('Me²'). Five months (*Infinity* p. 251)

58 He had earned two promotions and was now officer class. (*Backwards* p. 119)

59 Six years. (*Infinity* p. 17)

60 Triangles. ('Meltdown')

61 Five feet two. (*Better Than Life* p. 69)

62 Eau de Yak Urine. ('Back to Reality')

63 A dozen, twice as many as necessary. (*Backwards* p. 105)

64 Rogerson. (*Infinity* p. 43)

65 He was a chef. ('Ouroboros')

66 8.30 for 9.00. (*Infinity* p. 251)

67 His condominium on Venus. (*Backwards* p. 127)

68 Lady Sabrina Mulholland-Jjones. ('Timeslides')

69 Project Wildflower. (*Backwards* p. 122)

70 Fifteen. ('Meltdown')

71 Kochanski's Dave from a parallel universe. ('Blue')

72 Deck Sergeant. ('Holoship')

73 Twenty-five minutes. (*Infinity* p. 284)

74 He ran across the parade-ground singing the theme from *The Dambusters* and bombed the guard-post with luminous, urine-filled condoms; stole a motorcycle from the compound and scrawled obscenities over the ornamental garden in tyre marks; and stapled the penis of one of Ace's colleagues to his groin. (*Backwards* p. 121)

75 Todhunter. ('Duct Soup')
76 Flight Co-ordinator. ('The End')
77 Seven. (*Last Human* p. 147)
78 Bexley. ('Future Echoes')
79 Ace Rimmer. ('Stoke Me a Clipper')
80 Thirty-seven. (*Backwards* p. 119)
81 Five and four. ('Meltdown')
82 A winch. ('Confidence and Paranoia', or *Infinity* p. 112)
83 Europa. (*Backwards* p. 110)
84 Rimmer. ('Dimension Jump')
85 He aches for more responsibility, constantly fails the engineering exam, astoundingly zealous, possibly mad, probably has more teeth than brain cells, promotion prospects – comical. ('Waiting for God')
86 Dieter Tranter's. (*Backwards* p. 128)
87 Supply Officer. ('Epideme')
88 A mutual interest in consuming ridiculous amounts of alcohol. (*Infinity* p. 104)
89 Sixteen. (*Backwards* p. 146)
90 Burma. ('Queeg')
91 Admiral. (*Backwards* p. 84)
92 Miss Anne ('Kryten'). Miss Yvette (*Infinity* p. 183).
93 Yvonne McGruder. ('Thanks for the Memory', or *Infinity* p. 247)
94 'Life is like a joss-stick, it stinks and then it's over.' (*Better Than Life* p. 67)
95 Six. ('Better Than Life', or *Infinity* p. 70)
96 Rimmer's hypnotherapist. ('Marooned')
97 A pink gingham dress, with red nail polish on its hoofs. (*Backwards* p. 43)

 98 Servicing dodgem cars in a fourth-rate travelling fair.
    (*Backwards* p. 110)
 99 Rimmer's mum. ('Polymorph')
100 Sergeant. ('Meltdown')
101 Wednesday. (*Backwards* p. 169)
102 CGI. ('Back to Reality')
103 Tim. ('Ouroboros')
104 The hillbilly. (*Backwards* p. 47)
105 Flight Engineer. ('Dimension Jump')
106 Ms Harrison's. ('Holoship')
107 One hour. ('Gunmen of the Apocalypse')
108 A shelf prop. (*Backwards* p. 63)
109 At Cadet School. ('Marooned')
110 Ten years' wages. (*Infinity* p. 295)
111 Bungo. (*Backwards* p. 84)
112 A bloke who fits windows. ('Timeslides')

Word search 8

'Duct Soup'

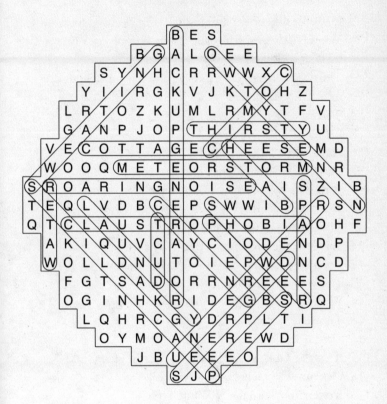

'Pussycat Willum!'

1 It was upside down and inside out. ('Waiting for God')
2 Sideways-pressed flares and a clip-on polyester tie. ('Tikka to Ride')
3 Thirty-six changes of clothing and ten full-length dress mirrors. ('Marooned')
4 The escort boots. ('Justice')
5 Eleven. ('Future Echoes')
6 Have half a juggling lesson. ('Epideme')
7 His lunch. ('Confidence and Paranoia')
8 A moron convention. ('Backwards')
9 Behind the fridge. ('Thanks for the Memory')
10 The green paisley shirt. ('Blue')
11 Seven in the morning. ('Better Than Life')
12 Twenty-eight hours. ('Emohawk – Polymorph II')
13 The one-armed bandit. ('Nanarchy')
14 With his tongue. ('Confidence and Paranoia')
15 Thursday. ('Epideme')
16 Two. ('Polymorph')
17 If you're God, why *that* face? ('Waiting for God')
18 One week. ('Demons and Angels')
19 Kryten and Rimmer. ('White Hole')
20 Eat him. ('Waiting for God')
21 Napkin rings, a box of hairnet requisition forms, a motorized tie rack and an inflatable shark. ('Nanarchy')
22 Surf boards. ('Thanks for the memory')
23 Twelve. ('Dimension Jump')
24 Kryten. ('Tikka to Ride')
25 Creature polo. (*Better Than Life* p. 18)

Jigword
'Tongue-tied'

'I'm on the cop'

1 Yvonne McGruder. (*Last Human* p. 106)
2 A horse. (*Better Than Life* p. 4)
3 He would become mega-rich and be forced to have constant sex with Lady Sabrina Mulholland-Jjones. ('Timeslides')
4 Twenty-two. ('Duct Soup')
5 Lister. ('Confidence and Paranoia')

6 It entitled them to choose the partner they desired. (*Last Human* p. 67)

7 Michael McGruder's girlfriend. (*Last Human* p. 277)

8 A device invented by bank managers to make us over-drawn. ('Confidence and Paranoia')

9 Bun-bun or Cheese. (*Backwards* p. 84)

10 Fifteen. (*Backwards* p. 146)

11 Go bobbing for apples in a communal latrine at the Reading Festival. ('Blue')

12 His rubber plant. ('Balance of Power')

13 In a plane crash while making love to his fourteenth wife. ('Timeslides')

14 Lindy Lou. (*Backwards* p. 146)

15 Because he let his mum buy all his casual clothes. ('Confidence and Paranoia')

16 Lise Yates. ('Thanks for the Memory')

17 He used to put his nan's bras around the armchair. ('Blue')

18 Napoleon. (*Infinity* p. 107)

19 The bald bloke who used to serve the fish. ('Duct Soup')

20 Love. ('Confidence and Paranoia')

21 Lister. ('Polymorph')

22 Marrying a dead man. (*Infinity* p. 280)

23 Mamie. (*Backwards* p. 80)

24 He gets horny. ('Blue')

25 Give it a love bite. (*Better Than Life* p. 4)

26 Titan Zoo. ('Kryten')

27 His telescope. ('Thanks for the Memory')

28 Kochanski. ('Duct Soup')

29 A girl called Sandra. ('Marooned')

30 Lick Lindy Lou's armpits for ten seconds. (*Backwards* p. 146)

31 Twelve hours. ('Stoke Me a Clipper')

32 A business trip to Hawaii. ('Confidence and Paranoia')

33 To have sex. ('Gunmen of the Apocalypse')

34 He found the love letter she had sent Lister. ('Thanks for the Memory')

35 He'd go with Betty but he'd be thinking of Wilma. ('Backwards')

36 Being stuck opposite Brigitte Nielsen in a packed lift. ('The Last Day')

37 Five days. (*Better Than Life* p. 15)

38 That she had been killed in a road accident earlier in the evening. (*Infinity* p. 252)

39 Someone called Tiffany who drank Campari and soda. ('Ouroboros')

40 Because he couldn't get a date. ('Confidence and Paranoia')

41 Twice. ('Holoship')

42 Lister's. ('The Last Day')

43 In Trixie LaBouche's handbag. (*Better Than Life* p. 37)

44 Acapulco. ('Timeslides')

45 Rimmer. ('Holoship')

46 Taramasalata. ('Dimension Jump')

47 Number Four. ('Duct Soup')

48 Carol McCauley's. ('Stasis Leak')

49 Next Wednesday morning. ('Holoship')

50 In Lister's dream. ('Blue')

51 Fifteen. ('The Inquisitor')

52 A woman. ('Rimmerworld')

53 A lifetime. ('Gunmen of the Apocalypse')

54 Three. (*Last Human* p. 194)
55 Rimmer. ('Ouroboros')
56 Lorraine. ('Parallel Universe')
57 The simulant. ('Justice')

'There's a wise old cat saying which I think applies in this situation'

 1 Pete Tranter's sister. ('Psirens')
 2 Kryten. ('Blue')
 3 Rimmer. ('Dimension Jump')
 4 Cat. ('Nanarchy')
 5 Cat. ('Bodyswap')
 6 Talkie Toaster. ('Future Echoes')
 7 Rimmer. ('Tikka to Ride')
 8 Rimmer. ('Confidence and Paranoia')
 9 Rimmer. ('Demons and Angels')
10 Cat. ('Justice')
11 Lister. ('Epideme')
12 High Kryten. ('Demons and Angels')
13 Lister. ('Duct Soup')
14 Holly. ('Dimension Jump')
15 Rimmer 2. ('Me²')
16 Kryten. ('Nanarchy')
17 Cat. ('DNA')
18 Rimmer. ('Me²')
19 Cat. ('Thanks for the Memory')
20 Cat. ('Beyond a Joke')

21 Rimmer. ('Emohawk – Polymorph II')
22 Rimmer. ('The End')
23 Lister. ('Epideme')
24 Rimmer. ('Psirens')
25 Cat. ('Terrorform')
26 Kochanski. ('Nanarchy')
27 Rimmer. ('Thanks for the Memory')
28 Cat. ('Beyond a Joke')
29 Rimmer. ('Future Echoes')
30 Lister. ('Holoship')
31 Rimmer. ('Quarantine')
32 Lister. ('Beyond a Joke')
33 Cat. ('The Inquisitor')
34 Rimmer. ('Back to Reality')
35 Lister. ('Blue')
36 Holly. ('Kryten')
37 Lister. ('The Last Day')
38 Kochanski. ('Ouroboros')
39 Rimmer. ('Waiting for God')
40 Cat. ('Backwards')
41 Ace Rimmer. ('Stoke Me a Clipper')
42 Cat. ('Terrorform')
43 Spare Head Two. ('Tikka to Ride')
44 Rimmer. ('Thanks for the Memory')
45 Rimmer. ('Marooned')
46 Kryten. ('Epideme')
47 Rimmer. ('Me^2')
48 Kryten. ('White Hole')
49 Cat. ('Duct Soup')
50 Kryten. ('Meltdown')
51 Cat. ('Stasis Leak')

52 Ace Rimmer. ('Dimension Jump')

53 Holly. ('Future Echoes')

54 Lister. ('Out of Time')

55 Lister. ('Ouroboros')

56 Genny mutant. ('Polymorph')

57 Holly. ('Back to Reality')

58 Holly. ('Confidence and Paranoia')

59 Kochanski. ('Blue')

60 Holly. ('Balance of Power')

61 Lister. ('Waiting for God')

62 Lister. ('Nanarchy')

63 Rimmer. ('Polymorph')

64 Lister. ('Kryten')

65 Kryten. ('Psirens')

66 Lister. ('Tikka to Ride')

67 Andy. ('Back to Reality')

68 Lister. ('The Inquisitor')

69 Lister. ('Beyond a Joke')

70 Kryten. ('Quarantine')

71 Rimmer. ('Stasis Leak')

72 Cat. ('Duct Soup')

73 Cat. ('Parallel Universe')

74 Lister. ('Bodyswap')

75 Mrs Bennett. ('Beyond a Joke')

76 Cat. ('The Last Day')

77 Cat. ('Ouroboros')

78 Cat. ('Demons and Angels')

79 Better Than Life host. ('Better Than Life')

80 Young Lister. ('Timeslides')

81 Lister. ('Epideme')

82 Rimmer. ('Waiting for God')

83 The Dog. ('Parallel Universe')
84 Rimmer. ('Balance of Power')
85 Lister. ('Duct Soup')
86 Cat. ('Tikka to Ride')
87 Rimmer. ('Better Than Life')
88 Able. ('Beyond a Joke')
89 Holly. ('White Hole')
90 Rimmer. ('Balance of Power')
91 Holly. ('Nanarchy')
92 Cat. ('Terrorform')
93 Rimmer. ('Balance of Power')
94 Rimmer. ('Parallel Universe')

Word search 9
Characters

'What are you looking for?'

1 Triangular. ('Better Than Life')
2 Level 159. ('The End')
3 The left arm. ('Stoke Me a Clipper')
4 On his right wrist. ('Confidence and Paranoia')
5 His left hand. ('Kryten')
6 Two. ('Tikka to Ride')
7 The left hand and the right eye. ('Terrorform')
8 A round, green tin. ('Better Than Life')
9 Jim. ('Future Echoes')
10 Yellow furry dice. ('Thanks for the Memory')
11 The right boot. ('Blue')
12 The bottom of a saucepan. ('Emohawk – Polymorph II')
13 Copal. ('Queeg')
14 Season 29. ('Balance of Power')
15 Six. ('Stoke Me a Clipper')
16 A meat pie. ('The End')
17 Four fish. ('Thanks for the Memory')
18 A *Spot the Dog* book. ('Kryten')
19 In his right eye. ('Confidence and Paranoia')
20 Gary. ('Kryten')
21 Seven balls and two cues. ('Ouroboros')
22 L, K and C. ('Dimension Jump')
23 His left ear. ('Tikka to Ride')
24 Three. ('Thanks for the Memory')
25 Eight. ('Kryten')
26 Red tartan. ('Balance of Power')
27 K177. ('White Hole')
28 A tureen of tomato soup. ('Kryten')

29 His right nostril. ('Ouroboros')
30 An electric carving knife. ('Bodyswap')
31 When it is on his chef's hat. ('Better Than Life')
32 Landing deck B. ('Stoke Me a Clipper')
33 Triangular. ('Psirens')
34 His left hand. ('The Inquisitor')
35 Anticlockwise. ('Back to Reality')
36 The right breast pocket of his jacket. ('Blue')
37 Twenty-four. ('Kryten')
38 Heart-shaped. ('Timeslides')
39 Saturn. ('Confidence and Paranoia')
40 Better than Life. ('Better Than Life')
41 A white carrier bag. ('Tikka to Ride')
42 While getting ready to board the *Nova 5*. ('Kryten')
43 A currant tin. ('Polymorph')
44 Two. ('Better Than Life')
45 Mapping Officer. ('Kryten')
46 Star Airways. ('Tikka to Ride')
47 CCD 517.3. ('White Hole')
48 *Red Dwarf*. ('Thanks for the Memory')
49 Hanging by Lister's bunk. ('Better Than Life')
50 In a disintegrator. ('Ouroboros')
51 His left hand. ('The End')
52 The left side. ('Back to Reality')
53 H7-6319. ('Beyond a Joke')
54 In the dining-room on the *Nova 5*. ('Kryten')
55 Peach slices. ('Duct Soup')
56 To the memory of the memory of Lise Yates. ('Thanks for the Memory')
57 'Tomorrow is the first day of the rest of your death.' ('Me^2')

58 2000 gigawatts. ('Queeg')
59 On the back of his left hand. ('Balance of Power')
60 A hamster in a wheel. ('Stoke Me a Clipper')
61 Cat. ('Kryten')
62 Four. ('Parallel Universe')
63 The right front wing. ('Tikka to Ride')
64 His left leg. ('Marooned')
65 His pink suit. ('Better Than Life')
66 Three times. ('Epideme')
67 Six. ('Gunmen of the Apocalypse')
68 From the left. ('Polymorph')
69 Rimmer's. ('Timeslides')
70 Toodle Pipski. ('Blue')
71 When Kryten 'tidied up'. ('Kryten')
72 Level 348. ('Future Echoes')
73 Six. ('Tikka to Ride')
74 Lister. ('Dimension Jump')
75 His left temple. ('Bodyswap')
76 California. ('Better Than Life')
77 The right one was white, and the left one was black. ('Waiting for God')
78 His right cuff. ('Beyond a Joke')
79 Three. ('Confidence and Paranoia')
80 With a sieve. ('Future Echoes')
81 DATE. ('Bodyswap')
82 Anne Gill. ('Kryten')
83 A chicken. ('DNA')
84 Her right leg. ('Ouroboros')
85 Three. ('Back to Reality')
86 25. ('Justice')
87 A Deluxe Keystone. ('Tikka to Ride')

88 With her teeth. ('Gunmen of the Apocalypse')

89 The left arm. ('Epideme')

90 One. ('Parallel Universe')

91 'Bonehead'. ('Dimension Jump')

92 When he was 'courting'. ('Me^2')

93 From the right. ('Epideme')

94 Books, a mug, a toilet roll and a photograph. ('The Inquisitor')

95 Two beer bottles. ('Polymorph')

96 Jane Air. ('Kryten')

97 In a kidney bowl. ('Tikka to Ride')

98 'Wear this.' ('The Last Day')

99 His name surrounded by pink flowers. ('Confidence and Paranoia')

100 Magenta. ('Terrorform')

101 When Lister was giving Rimmer some of his memory. ('Thanks for the Memory')

102 His left cheek. ('Parallel Universe')

103 'Smeghead'. ('Ouroboros')

104 VOTE 1. ('Back to Reality')

105 The triangle. ('Demons and Angels')

106 The nail of the little finger on his right hand. ('Psirens')

107 Lister's grandmother. ('Future Echoes')

108 His right shoulder. ('Tikka to Ride')

109 Six. ('Timeslides')

110 One. ('Thanks for the Memory')

111 Three. ('The End')

112 Confidence was eating a fried breakfast, and Paranoia was eating a yoghurt. ('Confidence and Paranoia')

113 Five. ('Epideme')

114 Two. ('Stasis Leak')
115 26 November 2155. ('Ouroboros')
116 161 cm. ('Kryten')
117 Four. ('Me²')
118 Three. ('Dimension Jump')
119 12.27. ('Tikka to Ride')

Word grid 1

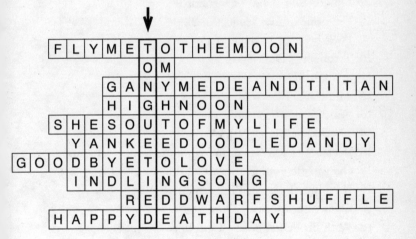

'Officer Bud Babe!'

1 In the trendiest part of Glasgow. ('Duct Soup')

2 Some brunette in catering. (*Infinity* p. 71)

3 Because he thinks that she is not good enough for Lister. ('Ouroboros')

4 Going down to the laundry room to watch her knickers spin dry. ('Duct Soup')

5 Went through a whole box of tissues. ('Nanarchy')

6 What 'off-side' was. ('Duct Soup')

7 Officer Bud Babe. ('Ouroboros')

8 Diamonds. (*Last Human* p. 226)

9 Four hours. ('Balance of Power')

10 Trumper. ('Duct Soup')

11 Sixteen. (*Last Human* p. 38)

12 The Cat's. ('Beyond a Joke')

13 Nine years. (*Backwards* p. 48)

14 The Magic Flute. ('Blue')

15 Because he's great, an incredibly seductive, charming, charismatic young stud. ('Confidence and Paranoia')

16 A bedside manner. ('Epideme')

17 Over three weeks. ('Duct Soup')

18 With his dental floss. ('Ouroboros')

19 When she 'gets brave'. (*Last Human* p. 253)

20 Eleven. ('Duct Soup')

21 Fourteen. ('Beyond a Joke')

22 Rimmer. (*Last Human* p. 180)

Crossword 7
'The End'

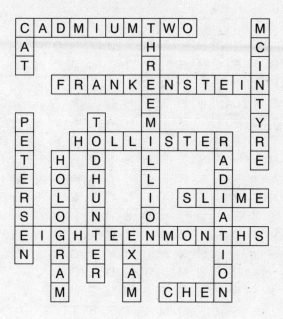

Word search 10
Kochanski

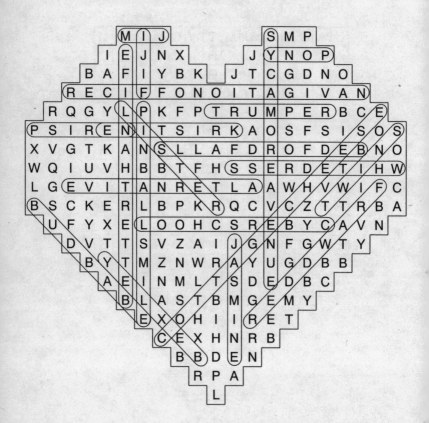

'Have infection, will travel'

1 In a place later called the Serengeti Plains, in northern Tanzania. (*Last Human* p. 2)
2 *St Elsewhere*. ('Camille')
3 Women crying. ('Duct Soup')
4 Because she needed an appendectomy. (*Last Human* p. 28)
5 Reason with it. ('Epideme')
6 The holovirus. ('Quarantine')
7 Doc MacKenzie. (*Infinity* p. 260)
8 With a hypodermic syringe. ('Nanarchy')
9 On his left shoulder. (*Better Than Life* p. 37)
10 Twenty-four hours. ('Stoke Me a Clipper')
11 Forty. (*Last Human* p. 104)
12 Half past three. ('Confidence and Paranoia')
13 99%. (*Last Human* p. 70)
14 When he fell into the cargo bay. ('Balance of Power')
15 Twenty-seven and one cap. (*Last Human* p. 191)
16 Twenty-four. ('Terrorform')
17 The skeleton in the medi-bay. ('Ourorobos')
18 The herd of short-haired yaks. (*Last Human* p. 88)
19 His brain was in a jar. ('Balance of Power')
20 Forty-eight hours. ('Epideme')
21 He drowned in sewage. (*Better Than Life* p. 132)
22 Parachutes. (*Last Human* p. 113)
23 Tied his hair to the bedpost and sounded the fire alarm. ('Me²')
24 It consumes its host. ('Epideme')

25 Enough to irrigate the Mooli Desert on Cyrius 3. (*Last Human* p. 130)

26 By radio waves. ('Quarantine')

27 A part-time evening job at a dentist's, having his filling replaced by student dentists. (*Last Human* p. 166)

28 His German language disk. ('Blue')

29 His right. (*Last Human* p. 110)

30 Old Doc Diagnostics. (*Backwards* p. 304)

31 Split-screen, slow motion, quantel, flips and strobing. (*Last Human* p. 238)

32 Three million years. ('Epideme')

33 Jellyfish and bank managers. ('Thanks for the Memory')

34 Dr Graham. ('Confidence and Paranoia')

35 Four hours. (*Last Human* p. 217)

36 Toothache and a boil on the inside of his left nostril. (*Last Human* p. 84)

37 By cutting off his arm. ('Epideme')

38 Twenty. ('Terrorform')

39 Old age. ('Ouroboros')

40 Rimmer. (*Last Human* p. 105)

41 His dart landed in the back of Kryten's head. ('Quarantine')

42 Thursday 21st at eleven thirty. (*Better Than Life* p. 228)

43 The middle classes. ('Better Than Life')

44 Malaria. ('Epideme')

45 It controls and manipulates the senses. (*Last Human* p. 19)

46 One month. ('Waiting for God')

47 Strips of material ripped from her blouse. (*Last Human* p. 249)

48 The one-armed man. ('Nanarchy')

49 Having your whole body vigorously rubbed by a man with a cheese grater. (*Infinity* p. 14)

50 Three weeks. ('Justice')

51 Sergeant Arden Reinhardt's. (*Backwards* p. 122)

52 Winnie-the-Pooh. ('Meltdown')

53 Fifty-eight minutes. ('Epideme')

54 A St Christopher medal. (*Backwards* p. 83)

55 Planning. (*Last Human* p. 89)

56 0.00000004321, an all-year low. (*Last Human* p. 76)

57 Amnesia. ('Psirens')

58 His nose, his left leg and his penis. (*Backwards* p. 314)

59 Holly. ('Me^2')

60 Drowning. (*Last Human* p. 121)

61 As a rival to the nicotine patch to block all neural signals relating to nicotine craving. ('Epideme')

62 In his mid-twenties. ('Future Echoes')

63 Seppuku. ('Back to Reality')

64 With a laser bone saw. ('Epideme')

65 Just under four miles an hour. (*Last Human* p. 247)

66 The knight from the AR machine. ('Stoke Me a Clipper')

67 He fed him into the waste grinder and flushed his mince into space. ('Confidence and Paranoia')

68 He had six ribs uncracked and had chronic pain lifted from his kidneys. (*Backwards* p. 62)

69 Lithium carbonate. ('Back to Reality')

70 Break both his legs and pull off his thumbs. ('Better Than Life')

71 Spare Head Three. (*Last Human* p. 243)

72 At an Italian field hospital. ('The Last Day')

73 Neurones which run up to the left hemisphere of his brain. ('Nanarchy')

74 It decapitated him. (*Backwards* p. 324)

75 She was knocked down by a truck. ('Beyond a Joke')

76 Blood and adrenalin. ('Epideme')

77 As a pile of albino mouse droppings. ('The End')

78 Wood glue. ('Ouroboros')

79 Brassica 2 – creates fast-growing broccoli. (*Last Human* p. 227)

80 Silicon rickets. ('DNA')

81 His left earlobe. (*Better Than Life* p. 136)

82 Because the King of the Potato people wouldn't let him. ('Quarantine')

83 Ninety minutes. (*Last Human* p. 87)

84 Physical torture. ('Terrorform')

85 Bangalore belly. ('Legion')

86 7%. ('Epideme')

87 Eighteen. (*Last Human* p. 44)

88 Lister. ('Duct Soup')

89 All four of his third molars. (*Last Human* p. 192)

90 He felt the urge to suffocate himself with a two-pound black ribbed knobbler. ('Dimension Jump')

91 Two bottles of anaesthetic, a roll of gauze and a nurse's hat. (*Last Human* p. 49)

92 In his navel. (*Better Than Life* p. 13)

93 The left hemisphere. ('Nanarchy')

94 $£700,000. (*Better Than Life* p. 41)

'Why did I always turn to page 47 and start drawing little beards and moustaches on the sperms?'

1 Lister. (*Backwards* p. 44)

2 Ace Rimmer. (*Backwards* p. 95)

3 Ace Rimmer. (*Backwards* p. 123)

4 Rimmer. (*Backwards* p. 153)

5 Rimmer. (*Better Than Life* p. 3)

6 Holly. (*Backwards* p. 188)

7 Cat. (*Better Than Life* p. 81)

8 Cat. (*Infinity* p. 222)

9 Michael McGruder. (*Last Human* p. 223)

10 Cat. (*Backwards* p. 305)

11 John Ewe. (*Better Than Life* p. 128)

12 Pizzak' Rapp. (*Backwards* p. 261)

13 Reketrebn. (*Last Human* p. 173)

14 Ace Rimmer. (*Backwards* p. 81)

15 Cat. (*Backwards* p. 299)

16 Rimmer. (*Backwards* p. 158)

17 Rimmer. (*Infinity* p. 25)

18 Kryten. (*Backwards* p. 210)

19 Kochanski. (*Last Human* p. 209)

20 Petersen. (*Backwards* p. 118)

21 Jim. (*Better Than Life* p. 9)

22 Kryten. (*Infinity* p. 187)

23 Cat. (*Backwards* p. 134)

24 Mrs Thornton (Old Prune Face). (*Last Human* p. 146)

25 Holly. (*Better Than Life* p. 35)

26 Pestilence. (*Backwards* p. 304)

27 Kryten. (*Last Human* p. 234)
28 Ace Rimmer. (*Backwards* p. 80)
29 Rimmer. (*Backwards* p. 335)
30 Petersen. (*Infinity* p. 39)
31 Kryten. (*Last Human* p. 238)
32 Kryten. (*Better Than Life* p. 210)
33 Death. (*Backwards* p. 327)
34 Lister. (*Infinity* p. 32)
35 Kochanski. (*Last Human* p. 89)
36 Cat. (*Better Than Life* p. 19)
37 Cat. (*Backwards* p. 156)
38 Lister. (*Backwards* p. 198)
39 Lister. (*Infinity* p. 114)
40 Kryten. (*Last Human* p. 208)
41 Rimmer's body-tailor. (*Better Than Life* p. 14)
42 Kryten. (*Backwards* p. 204)
43 Tonto Jitterman. (*Better Than Life* p. 65)
44 Denis. (*Infinity* p. 20)
45 Cat. (*Better Than Life* p. 169)

Crossword 8
'Nanarchy'

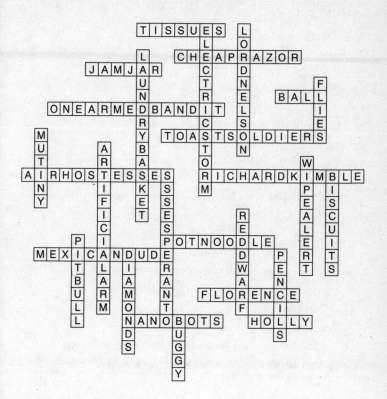

'Get my information from the Junior Colour Encyclopaedia of Space. The respect you have for me is awesome, innit?'

1 Because the Earth's pole star had changed. (*Infinity* p. 17)

2 A kind of protoplasmic broth from which all things evolved. (*Last Human* p. 168)

3 2,707 million miles. (*Infinity* p. 40)

4 *Red Dwarf.* ('Nanarchy')

5 Three nanoseconds. (*Last Human* p. 116)

6 On a dilapidated class three transport ship as a prisoner of the Gelf State. (*Last Human* p. 165)

7 On Pluto. (*Better Than Life* p. 130)

8 The Oblivion virus. (*Last Human* p. 93)

9 Delta 7. ('Epideme')

10 Like a tidal wave – go for the eye of the storm. ('Ouroboros')

11 Admiral Peter Tranter. (*Backwards* p. 127)

12 It powers the ship. It's a quantum drive. It allows you to leap from one point in space to another. (*Infinity* p. 208)

13 At the Forum of Justice on Arranguu 12. (*Last Human* p. 11)

14 Star Wars. (*Backwards* p. 161)

15 In the north-west. (*Last Human* p. 105)

16 A giant toupee. ('Marooned')

17 A bright young systems analyst at Android International. (*Better Than Life* p. 21)

The Answers

18 With jump leads from *Starbug*. ('Back to Reality')

19 Increase *Starbug*'s cabin temperature to 75 degrees centigrade. (*Last Human* p. 64)

20 Four points. (*Better Than Life* p. 130)

21 An ice gas. ('Blue')

22 A hurricane the size of Earth that howled relentlessly over its surface. (*Backwards* p. 100)

23 The point in space-time where all the different realities converge. It is the home to all the rejected time-lines and the entrance to all seven universes. (*Last Human* p. 34)

24 A phenomenon rarely seen in space that, legend would have us believe, transports us into another space and time. ('Backwards')

25 It kills electricity. (*Last Human* p. 107)

26 Because it's all black with twinkly bits. ('Nanarchy')

27 Mercury. ('Queeg')

28 One hundred light years long and one thousand light years deep. (*Last Human* p. 244)

29 The IQ of a single all-night car-park attendant. (*Better Than Life* p. 31)

30 Five and a half weeks. (*Last Human* p. 159)

31 Two years. (*Backwards* p. 118)

32 500 fathoms. (*Last Human* p. 205)

33 His highest levels of thought. (*Better Than Life* p. 45)

34 Lotomi 5. (*Last Human* p. 103)

35 Plexiglas. (*Backwards* p. 4)

36 Wolverhampton. (*Infinity* p. 15)

37 It had passed into the Omni-Zone. (*Last Human* p. 169)

38 Ace Rimmer, before giving it to Spanners. (*Backwards* p. 124)

39 Sand. ('Nanarchy')

40 Twenty-two hours earlier than Holly had anticipated. ('Future Echoes')

41 Pink. (*Last Human* p. 93)

42 Tuesday 5th. (*Better Than Life* p. 123)

43 2.2 million light years. (*Last Human* p. 157)

44 Navigating at light speed. ('Future Echoes')

45 669,600,000 miles per hour. (*Infinity* p. 132)

46 Six. (*Last Human* p. 12)

47 Venus. (*Better Than Life* p. 129)

48 At the Hilo Institute in Hawaii. (*Last Human* p. 209)

49 You get hit by a truck. (*Backwards* p. 106)

50 ZCSBFD6577GJG93857JJJJJ43767737837FHD-KWOPIW53. (*Last Human* p. 227)

51 The Holly Hop Drive. ('Parallel Universe')

52 From millions of years to barely three. (*Last Human* p. 168)

53 186,282. (*Better Than Life* p. 142)

54 45.265881. ('Queeg')

55 Their planet's erratic orbit and its position on the edge of the solar system. (*Better Than Life* p. 129)

56 A fortnight. ('Backwards')

57 To repair all the hydrogen molecules. (*Last Human* p. 156)

58 It's black. ('Marooned')

59 On Ganymede. (*Better Than Life* p. 128)

60 On the Saturnian moon Tethys. (*Infinity* p. 57)

61 Venus. (*Better Than Life* p. 129)

62 The Andromeda Galaxy. (*Last Human* p. 157)

63 Five. ('Marooned')

64 Not enough side. ('White Hole')

65 128. (*Infinity* p. 162)

66 Mars. (*Better Than Life* p. 129)

67 Two hundred barrels of oil, five bars of Gato or four millilitres of sperm. (*Last Human* p. 69)

68 Twenty minutes. ('Marooned')

69 It tunes in to an individual psyche and adapts its terrain to mimic its mental state. ('Terrorform')

70 Blue. (*Last Human* p. 94)

71 The point of no return. (*Better Than Life* p. 142)

72 Six days. ('Rimmerworld')

73 Non-space. ('Ouroboros')

74 On Arranguu 12. (*Last Human* p. 74)

75 It returns time and matter to the universe. ('White Hole')

76 Four hundred thousands years. (*Last Human* p. 154)

Word grid 2

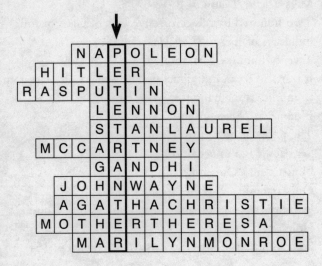

Number search

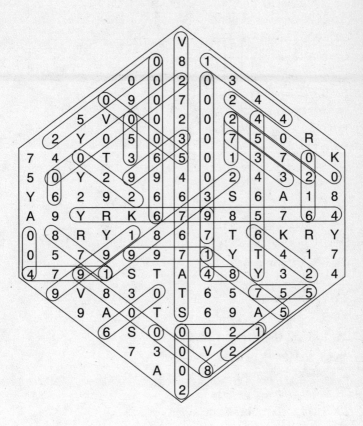

1 669600000 (*Infinity* p. 132)

2 YT6564354 (*Last Human* p. 136)

3 STA-7676-45-327-28V (*Last Human* p. 37)

4 1344 (*Infinity* p. 93)

5 6120 ('Holoship')

 6 25000 (*Infinity* p. 193)
 7 350 (*Infinity* p. 111)
 8 2000 (*Infinity* p. 240)
 9 5000 (*Infinity* p. 272)
10 246 (*Infinity* p. 144)
11 400 (*Infinity* p. 272)
12 3.37 (*Infinity* p. 221)
13 46758976KRY (*Last Human* p. 108)
14 1200 (*Better Than Life* p. 94)
15 60 (*Infinity* p. 186)
16 2572 (*Infinity* p. 210)
17 793000000 (*Infinity* p. 13)
18 4179 (*Infinity* p. 35)
19 220 (*Infinity* p. 261)
20 19.99 ('White Hole', or *Better Than Life* p. 157)
21 600 ('Rimmerworld')
22 84 ('Quarantine')
23 1799 (*Infinity* p. 272)
24 557 ('Rimmerworld')
25 198732 (*Infinity* p. 121)
26 369 (*Infinity* p. 365)
27 24000 ('Marooned')
28 9800 (*Infinity* p. 54)
29 2155 ('Ouroboros', or *Infinity* p. 32)
30 200000 (*Infinity* p. 131)
31 800 (*Infinity* p. 14)
32 172 ('Holoship')
33 871 ('Backwards')
34 1875 ('Gunmen of the Apocalypse')
35 1974 (*Infinity* p. 182)
36 128 (*Infinity* p. 162)

Inset

1 In some kind of stampede. ('Tikka to Ride')
2 A night and a day in the bed of the Queen of Camelot. ('Stoke Me a Clipper')
3 For keeping him sane. ('Stoke Me a Clipper')
4 Princess Bonjella. ('Stoke Me a Clipper')
5 The Gelfs. ('Duct Soup')
6 Like he's a pot of cottage cheese with pineapple chunks in. ('Duct Soup')
7 What 'off-side' was. ('Duct Soup')
8 One wellington boot and a box of a hundred assorted tampons that glow in the dark. ('Blue')
9 Rimmer. ('Blue')
10 A nine-hole course. ('Blue')
11 Pride and Prejudice World. ('Beyond a Joke')
12 Cat. ('Beyond a Joke')
13 The WW2 game. ('Beyond a Joke')
14 Kryten. ('Beyond a Joke')
15 Lister. ('Epideme')
16 The Albanian State Washing Machine Company. ('Last Human')

READ MORE IN PENGUIN

In every corner of the world, on every subject under the sun, Penguin represents quality and variety – the very best in publishing today.

For complete information about books available from Penguin – including Puffins, Penguin Classics and Arkana – and how to order them, write to us at the appropriate address below. Please note that for copyright reasons the selection of books varies from country to country.

In the United Kingdom: Please write to *Dept. EP, Penguin Books Ltd, Bath Road, Harmondsworth, West Drayton, Middlesex UB7 ODA*

In the United States: Please write to *Consumer Sales, Penguin USA, P.O. Box 999, Dept. 17109, Bergenfield, New Jersey 07621-0120.* VISA and MasterCard holders call 1-800-253-6476 to order Penguin titles

In Canada: Please write to *Penguin Books Canada Ltd, 10 Alcorn Avenue, Suite 300, Toronto, Ontario M4V 3B2*

In Australia: Please write to *Penguin Books Australia Ltd, P.O. Box 257, Ringwood, Victoria 3134*

In New Zealand: Please write to *Penguin Books (NZ) Ltd, Private Bag 102902, North Shore Mail Centre, Auckland 10*

In India: Please write to *Penguin Books India Pvt Ltd, 706 Eros Apartments, 56 Nehru Place, New Delhi 110 019*

In the Netherlands: Please write to *Penguin Books Netherlands bv, Postbus 3507, NL-1001 AH Amsterdam*

In Germany: Please write to *Penguin Books Deutschland GmbH, Metzlerstrasse 26, 60594 Frankfurt am Main*

In Spain: Please write to *Penguin Books S. A., Bravo Murillo 19, 1° B, 28015 Madrid*

In Italy: Please write to *Penguin Italia s.r.l., Via Felice Casati 20, I–20124 Milano*

In France: Please write to *Penguin France S. A., 17 rue Lejeune, F–31000 Toulouse*

In Japan: Please write to *Penguin Books Japan, Ishikiribashi Building, 2–5–4, Suido, Bunkyo-ku, Tokyo 112*

In South Africa: Please write to *Longman Penguin Southern Africa (Pty) Ltd, Private Bag X08, Bertsham 2013*

READ MORE IN PENGUIN

Red Dwarf Grant Naylor

When Lister got drunk, he got really drunk.

After celebrating his birthday with a Monopoly-board pub crawl around London, he came to in a burger bar on one of Saturn's moons, wearing a lady's pink Crimplene hat and a pair of yellow fishing waders, with no money and a passport in the name of 'Emily Berkenstein'.

Joining the Space Corps seemed a good idea. Red Dwarf, a clapped-out spaceship, was bound for Earth. It never made it, leaving Lister as the last remaining member of the human race, three million years from Earth, with only a dead man, a senile computer and a highly evolved cat for company.

They begin their journey home. On the way they'll break the Light Barrier. They'll meet Einstein, Archimedes, God and Norman Wisdom . . . and discover an alternative plane of Reality.

Better Than Life Grant Naylor

Lister is lost. Three million years from Earth he's marooned in a world created by his own psyche. For Lister it's the most dangerous place he could possibly be because he's completely happy.

Rimmer has a problem too. He's dead. But that's not the problem. Rimmer's problem is that he's trapped in a landscape controlled by his own subconscious. And Rimmer's subconscious doesn't like him one little bit.

Together with Cat, the best-dressed entity in all six known universes, and Kryten, a sanitation Mechanoid with a missing sanity chip, they are trapped in the ultimate computer game: Better Than Life. The zenith of computer-game technology, BTL transports you directly to a perfect world of your imagination, a world where you can enjoy fabulous wealth and unmitigated success.

It's the ideal game – with only one drawback: it's so good, it'll kill you.

Also published in one volume as the **Red Dwarf Omnibus**

READ MORE IN PENGUIN

Last Human   Doug Naylor

Somewhere along the line, Lister had made a major mistake.

Why else would he find himself on a prison ship bound for Cyberia, the most inhospitable penal colony in Deep Space, sentenced to eighteen years' Hard Thought.

Dave Lister – the LAST HUMAN

The future of the species is in the hands of one man. And all he has to help him are his wits, his cunning, and a two-page girdle section from a mail-order catalogue.

'Smegging wonderful ... some of the comic riffs are sublime' – *Independent*

Backwards   Rob Grant

Dave Lister has finally found his way back to planet Earth. Which is good.

What's bad is that time isn't running in quite the right direction. And if he doesn't get off the planet soon, he's going to have to go through puberty again. Backwards.

Still, his crewmates have come to rescue him. Which is good.

Rejoin the trepid band of space zeroes from *Red Dwarf* and *Better Than Life* – Lister, Rimmer, Holly and the Cat – as they continue their epic journey through frontal-lobe-knotting realities where none dare venture but the bravest of the brave, the boldest of the bold, the feeblest of the feeble-minded.

READ MORE IN PENGUIN

Red Dwarf Quiz Book   Sharon Burnett and Nicky Hooks

'This sounds like a twelve change of underwear trip!'

Gather yours together and prepare to launch into the ultimate *Red Dwarf* experience. Call yourself a fan? Can you remember: When is Gazpacho Soup Day? What is Space Corps Directive 196156? Who said, 'That's it, we're deader than tank tops!'? The *Red Dwarf Quiz Book* is bursting with tantalizing trivia and quirky questions. Enough to keep you amused for several thousand light years.

Primordial Soup   Grant Naylor

Before recorded Time, there existed a substance known as Primordial Soup. From this disgustingly unpromising, gunky substance, all life began. Likewise, from the disgustingly unpromising, gunky scripts, sprang the disgusting, gunky comedy series, *Red Dwarf*.

Primordial Soup is a selection of the least worst scripts from the first five years of *Red Dwarf*, tracing the series from its humble beginnings to its humble present.

Each of the scripts has been personally chosen by the author from his rubber-sheeted bed in the Norfolk Nursing Home for the Intellectually Challenged.

Son of Soup   Rob Grant and Doug Naylor

Son of Soup contains a chunky new selection of freshly hand-picked scripts, one from each of the first six seasons. Its ingredients are: amusing jokes, reasonably interesting plots, bits that were cut out of the TV shows and candid photographs. All in all, it's an irresistible second helping of the least worst scripts – and it even comes with reading instructions.